CW00542246

Edited by
J. T. Greensmith

ISBN 0 900717 72 6

Iceland

CONTENTS

PREFACE

This guide is based on a series of visits to Iceland organised by Birkbeck College (University of London) Centre for Extra-Mural Studies. Two of these (1986 and 1993) were in collaboration with The Geologists' Association.

We are grateful to those who took part in these visits and to the authors of all the books and papers from which we have drawn knowledge and inspiration. In the former category we would single out for special mention Trausti Steinsson, Lindsay Marsh, Armann Hoskuldsson, Margaret Rusbridge, Ian Kille, Edward Finch and Stella Bignold. While the long list of the latter is best seen in the reference list, we must mention the late Sigidur Thorarinsson and Thorleifur and Trausti Eirarsson as major contributors and also George P.L. Walker who first showed one of us (JFP) Iceland and has, through his writings, been a major inspiration for this work.

Iceland

INTRODUCTION

While it is possible to carry out a limited study of some aspects of the geology of Iceland by selecting one base e.g. Reykjavik (Figure 27) or the Myvatn area (Figure 20), this guide is based on the assumption that visitors will be touring and spending a maximum of three nights in any one location. Access will normally be by air, arriving at Keflavik airport some 40km southwest of Reykjavik. It is possible to arrive by sea at a variety of locations, but this is not considered in this guide. Roads in Iceland are mainly dirt roads with occasional large stones and potholes. However, an increasing length of The Ring Road (Highway 1, the circum-Iceland route) is being covered by tarmacadam, while the mountain roads (those with an F prefix) and some of the remote rural routes are only passable to high clearance vehicles. This is due to the extreme roughness of the surface and the frequency of deep river crossings in some places. When hiring vehicles, therefore, groups should check that they have adequate clearance if using such routes. Most Icelandic coaches have radio or telephone links with Reykjavik and this is also essential if travelling into the interior. Finger posts, with road numbers and place names are common and, apart from some of the most remote locations, usually dependable. They should be used in conjunction with a good map, such as the 1:500,000 touring map of The Icelandic Geodetic Survey. A compass is also beneficial.

The best season to visit Iceland for maximum geological benefit is from mid-July until the end of August. Many sites may be visited over a much longer period, but late-lying snow and the presence of muddy sections on some roads prevents easy access to some interior sites until late July. Details of 'closed areas' are posted at petrol filling stations and at tourist information centres in towns.

The high latitude (Iceland is all SOUTH of the Arctic Circle) gives long daylight hours during the summer months. The temptation to continue visiting until dark is great and may need to be curbed in the interest of a night's rest!

There are three possible ways of arranging overnight accommodation while touring. Camping is popular, but the designated sites soon fill and for parties of more than six it is always advisable to book in advance. Roadside camping is not advised. Setting up and striking camp, and meal preparation, takes up time which some groups may prefer to spend visiting geological sites. Secondly, there are community and school halls which are open during the summer months for 'sleeping bag accommodation'. In these, you provide your own sleeping bag and sleep on mattresses, which are normally available, but usually on the floor. Finally, the most expensive

Michael Bamlett and John F. Potter

arrangement is to use hotels. Outside Reykjavik, there are few fully-equipped establishments, but during the summer months boarding schools operate as 'Edda Hotels', which are comfortable and quite well distributed throughout the country. There are also about 18 Youth Hostels and the same number of mountain huts.

If visitors choose to travel without the back-up of an Icelandic tour company, adequate stocks of food should be carried once Reykjavik is left behind, as suppliers are well scattered. It is strongly recommended that large groups should employ an Icelandic guide. These people know many of the key geological sites as they have usually taken a 'geology for tour guides' examination. Their main usefulness is as a negotiator and trouble shooter at camp sites and community halls, and as representatives of Iceland's culture. Leaders of geological groups should, however, make clear their priorities.

Icelandic place names are normally fairly consistent in their spelling, and some like Vik and Laugar are used many times. The Icelandic alphabet has four letters which do not appear in English, thus:

Icelandic letter þ pronounced as th in think

ð pronounced as th in the

œ pronounced as i in like

ö pronounced as i in bird

As English type faces do not have the first three of these, they will be written in this guide as th, d and ae respectively. The ö will be written as in Icelandic.

Geological maps of Iceland are produced by Landmaelingar Islands (Icelandic Geodetic Survey, 1993 address: Laugavegi 178, postholf 5060, 125 Reykjavik; telephone (91) 681611). This is also the source of the Touring Map referred to above. The Geological maps are on two scales (a) 1:500,000 for the whole country on a single sheet (1989) and (b) 1:250,000 (1 cm to 2.5 km) in a series covering the whole country on 9 sheets (some of these may be out of print at any given time). On these scales some of the categories of rock are not as precise as some petrologists might prefer, but they provide a sound basic outline of the country's surface outcrops.

As it is such a popular location for geological research, this type of work is controlled by the Government and intending researchers should discuss their proposals with the Iceland National Research Council, Laugavegi 13, Reykjavik. Icelandic geological research is particularly active in the fields of volcanic studies, igneous petrology, sedimentology, structural geology and

Quaternary/glaciology studies, so it must be accepted that views and

Iceland

interpretations are liable to change fairly rapidly.

THE GEOLOGICAL EVOLUTION OF ICELAND

Terms marked with an asterisk are explained further in the glossary. When the North Atlantic began to open, the present position of Iceland on the globe was covered by sea. As a function of that opening, the Mid-Atlantic Ridge developed. Iceland now lies on that feature, with a largely aseismic ridge extending southeastwards to the Faeroe Islands. At present, it appears that Iceland lies above a stationary hotspot or plume on the ridge, and volcanic activity is fed by irregular diapiric upwelling from the lower mantle. This upwelling seems to have commenced about 55 million years ago during the early Tertiary, as evidenced by the age of the most ancient rocks obtained from the sea bed cores from the Denmark Strait between Iceland and Greenland.

Volcanism in Iceland is mainly in the rift zones, but is also evident on some of the land outside the rifts. The rift volcanoes produce primitive tholeiites* (Mid-Ocean Ridge Basalts or MORB) at one end of their petro-graphic spectrum and high silicic rhyolites* and dacites* at the other. The non-rift zones erupt transitional to mildly alkaline (or in one case, calc-alka-line) lavas.

The rock types in the terrestrial rift zones are the same as those of the submerged rift zones, but with a greater volume and a higher degree of magmatic evolution. They include silicic lavas which are not found on the submerged ridge.

The oldest rocks which outcrop in Iceland are Tertiary basalts of about 16Ma (early Miocene), and the most recent at the time of writing were erupted from Hekla in January 1991. During the past 16 million years igneous rocks with a variety of compositions have been extruded and then moved east or west of the rift valley, which marks the central line of the Mid-Atlantic Ridge. The mechanism is known as sea-floor spreading. In the north of Iceland there is a single rift, but in the south there are two branch-es, with that on the west connecting with the Reykjanes Ridge of the main Mid-Atlantic Ridge (Figure 1). This western branch is currently less active than the eastern one, the latter containing the volcanic centres of Hekla, Torfajökull, Katla and Grimsvötn, all of which have been active during Pleistocene (glacial) and Holocene (post-glacial) times. The eastern branch continues seawards to The Westmann Islands (most recent eruption 1973) and Surtsey (new volcanic island 1967).

Michael Bamlett and John F. Potter

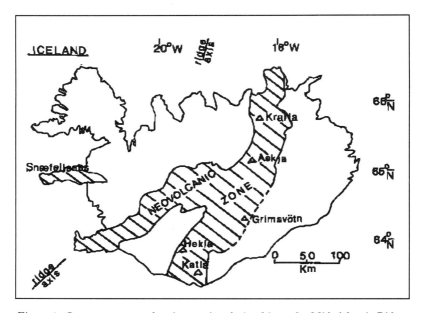

Figure 1. Quaternary neovolcanic zone in relationship to the Mid-Atlantic Ridge spreading axis.

Thus, in general, the oldest rocks lie either in the east or the west and northwest of the country (Figure 2). There are two exceptions. The Snaefellsnes peninsula, an apparent continuation of Tertiary volcanic activity into the Quaternary (see itinerary 11), was thought to be a spreading rift, but this is now regarded as incorrect. The other exception, though lacking activity during historic times, is the Skagaheidi peninsula in the north.

Iceland

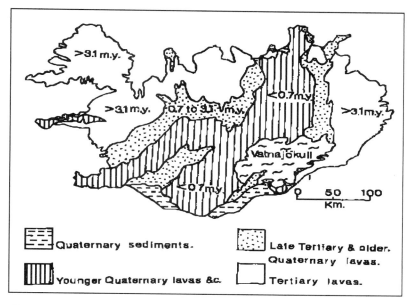

Figure 2: The main geological divisions of Iceland.

VOLCANIC-RELATED PHENOMENA OF THE ICELANDIC LANDSCAPE

The great majority of rocks in Iceland are of volcanic origin. The exceptions are alluvial deposits in the river valleys, glacial tills, the often fossiliferous deposits on raised beaches, a number of dried out lake-floor deposits and some wind-blown volcanic ash. All of these are composed predominantly of re-worked material which originated as lava or tephra*. Icelandic eruptions are characterised in textbooks as fissure eruptions. Many eruption sites are linear in form, but the actual effusion of lava or tephra comes from a series of closely spaced cones. There are also many apparently central-type volcanoes in Iceland. Many of the latter are either part of a row of cones, e.g. Krafla, or a particularly active localised series of craters e.g. Hekla.

Michael Bamlett and John F. Potter

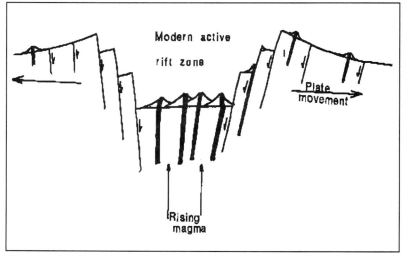

Figure 3: Doming, fissure eruptions and crustal extension.

Fissure eruptions occur at places where dykes reach the surface. Dykes are features of crustal extension and are common in rift valleys. The sideways movement of oceanic crustal plates provides space for the intrusion of molten rock which sometimes reaches the surface (see Figure 3 and Itineraries 5, 7 and 10).

A series of *cinder cones*, often as close as 25 m apart, marks the line of a fissure. Evidence of associated lava flows from the fissures can usually be seen on adjacent ground. See examples at Laki (Itinerary 3) and Leirnjukur (Itinerary 5). The cones themselves comprise explosively-generated tephra which was extruded simultaneously with the lava. Finer tephra (ash) may be found several kilometres from the line of the fissure. However, most ash or tuff* deposits originated in the major explosive activity of Hekla, Krafla and Askja, all of which are more like *central volcanoes* in their evolution and behaviour, with both silicic (=acid) and basaltic (=basic) phases providing Plinian* and Strombolian* activity as well as the more usual Icelandic fissure eruptions. *Caldera** formation has also taken place at, for example Askja (Itinerary 7) and Krafla (Itinerary 5).

There are *shield volcanoes* in the western and northern active zones, typified by the quiet extrusion of mobile olivine tholeiite* lava from a central vent. Skalbreidur (1060 m), and Baldheidi (771 m) are examples

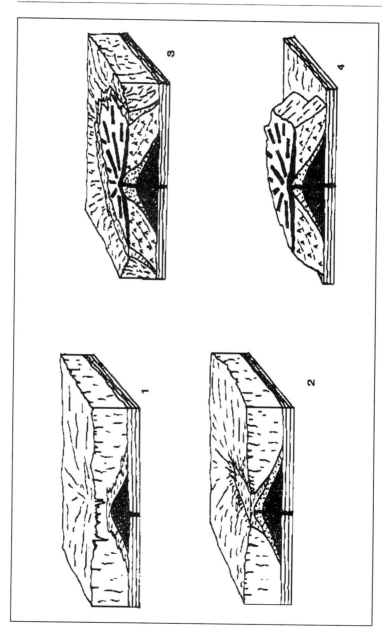

Figure 4: Origin of tuyas (after Jones, 1969). Explanation in text.

Michael Bamlett and John F. Potter

Another form of central activity is demonstrated by the *tuyas (Icelandic =stapis)* or table mountains. These were formed beneath ice sheets and, if developed subaerially, would have evolved as central volcanoes. Refer to Figure 4 in conjunction with the following description of their formation (after Jones, 1968). Initially, basaltic lava is erupted beneath ice, and the lobes of molten rock, in contact with melt water, develop a tough, plastic skin that is convex upwards. The lobes then burst, releasing molten material which then proceeds to form another lobe above the first, and the process may be repeated many times. These lobes comprise *pillow lavas* (Icelandic =bolstraberg), which ultimately form a conical pile with slumps around the margins (Figure 4/1). Some of the adjacent ice melts to form an englacial lake. As the lava pile builds up, the lake will eventually reach the ice surface, allowing Surtseyan* explosive activity to take place.

In succession to the pillow lavas, a pile of ash, with some fragments of disrupted pillows now develops (Figure 4/2). When the ash pile reaches the surface, subaerial lava flows succeed it, flowing quickly into the surrounding water and forming a roughly conical delta composed of hyaloclastite* (palagonite) around and above the pile of volcanic ash. As this delta builds up, more lava remains above the water level and this develops as a rigid cap above all the preceeding volcanic deposits. The lake is now roughly circular in form (Figure 4/3). Finally the surrounding ice melts and the distinctive form of the tuya is revealed (Figure 4/4). Examples include Herdubreid (1682 m) on Itinerary 7. Where acid lavas are extruded beneath ice, the resulting formation is a *rhyolite dome*, with large lobes of glassy rhyolite, sometimes occurring as black *obsidian*, in a granulated, vitrified matrix. An example is Bláfell (1222 m) southeast from Myvatn.

There are two types of small scale cones. *Spatter cones* occur when a lava flow is declining in its activity, but several pockets of hot material remain active. As they continue to bubble, they form small (normally about 10m diameter) 'boils' on the lava surface, comprising molten rock thrown into the air and falling back as 'spatter' close to the vent (e.g. in Eldgjá, Itinerary 14).

Tuff rings are cones made up of relatively fine volcaniclastic and pyroclastic material. They originate when magma reacts directly with groundwater close to the surface. The molten rock heats water to create steam which, under pressure, creates explosions at the surface. Fragments of new lava and older surface rocks are deposited in the vicinity of the eruption and display characteristic inward-dipping layers adjacent to the vent (Hrossaborg crater, Itinerary 4) (Cas & Wright, 1987).

Iceland

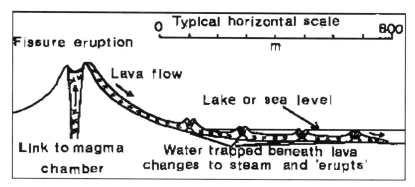

Figure 5: The structure and origin of rootless craters.

Rootless craters (also known as psuedo-craters or littoral cones) occur when a lava flow runs into shallow water or on to a saturated mud flat. Water trapped beneath the lava vaporises and explodes through the flow, causing small craters to form, usually in closely packed groups. They are not directly connected to a magma chamber and normally have only a single eruptive episode, although occasionally a smaller cone may develop inside the initial larger one towards the end of the event (see Skutustadir, Itinerary 5 and Figure 5 (Macdonald, 1972)).

On a smaller scale, where less water is involved e.g. a snow field or a marshy area, the craters are more like chimneys from the flow and are called *hornitos*. They are composed of volcaniclastic material and spatter.

LAVA FLOW FEATURES

The behaviour of lavas depends on the interaction of many variables. The most important of these are the chemistry of the melt, including its gas and water content, the temperature of the melt and of the adjacent ground and air, and the slope of the ground.

A basic (iron-magnesium-calcium dominated) lava will flow quickly and freely while its temperature remains above its melt point. ($c.1100°C$). Normally the base and the surface, being in contact with cooler materials, will cool first, insulating the fluid lava in the interior until it either cools and solidifies or runs out completely, leaving a void known as a *lava tube* or cave. The top surface of such a mobile flow will normally solidify as relatively smooth *ropy lava* with the characteristics of pahoehoe (Icelandic =helluhraun).

Michael Bamlett and John F. Potter

Rocks of similar chemistry, however, can form an aa (Icelandic =apalhraun) surface of irregular blocks over which it is difficult to walk. This occurs when a substantial volume of the flow has solidified and is a long way from the lava source, possibly on a low angle slope (e.g. Hekla 1970 flow, Itinerary 1).

Iceland is famous for its wealth of lavas featuring hexagonal *columnar joint structures*. While most of these are in basalts and tholeiites, there are some examples in rhyolites. These features form as a network of cooling centres at the lava-ground and lava-air interfaces. The best examples (e.g. Dverghamrar, Itinerary 2) are found where lava has erupted beneath a recently deposited blanket of tephra which compels a longer cooling period and thus better structures develop. These also demonstrate horizontal *chisel marks* which indicate the phases of cooling of the lava. Close examination will reveal plumose* strain markings which show the direction of breaking as the lava cooled and cracked along the joint planes. It should be remembered that all such columns are formed at 90° to the cooling surface which generates them. Curved columns are likely to be a function of slow deformation during the cooling period before the lava has set solid (see Figures 6 & 7 and DeGraff & Aydin, 1987; Long & Wood, 1986; Ryan & Sammis, 1978; Saemundsson, 1970).

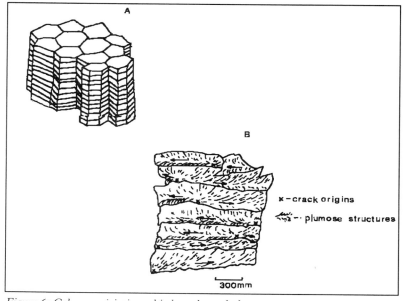

Figure 6: *Columnar jointing, chisel marks and plumose structure*

Iceland

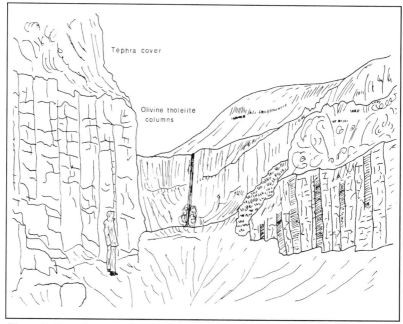

Figure 7: Dverghamrar - looking north (sketch from photograph).

Lava tumuli are features of some flows and are small mounds of lava punctuating the surface of the flow. They are usually cracked and slabs of rock are often displaced. Their formation is due to one of three causes (a) the surface of the lava cools but the lateral pressure exerted on it makes it bulge upwards, (b) fluid lava continues to flow under pressure, beneath the solid surface, occasionally causing upward bulging, and (c) the lava may have flowed over a pre-existing hump (Bamlett & Potter, 1988). Associated with lava tumuli are depressions in the lava surface, caused by the same sort of process as lava tubes, allowing a slab of cooled, solid lava to subside into a void after the fluid lava has run out.

When a hot lava flows into water the interaction between fluids produces a hyaloclastite (but see section on pillow lavas, above), which characteristically consists of yellow-brown cryptocrystalline material cementing larger fragments of the violently disrupted lava. Most of the Pleistocene lavas in Iceland were erupted under these conditions and thus have these properties. When weathered, these rocks are termed moberg and are of acid, intermediate or basic composition (see Landmannalaugar, Itinerary 14 and Jarlhettur, Itinerary 13; Honnorez & Kirst, 1975).

Michael Bamlett and John F. Potter

Many of the basaltic/tholeiitic lavas in Iceland are vesicular*, indicating a high gas content. The vesicles are commonly filled with what are probably secondary materials. In the Quaternary lavas the fillings are normally chalcedony*, but in the older Tertiary rocks minerals of the *zeolite group* are commonly found. In eastern Iceland Walker (1960) worked out a clearly zoned zeolite sequence, which is based on the principle of ascending geothermal groundwater giving rise to temperature controlled zeolite zones (Figure 8). Zeolites are hydrated silicates in which calcium and aluminium predominate, with subsidiary sodium and potassium. They result from the alteration of feldspars and aluminium-rich minerals during hydrothermal activity. See the museum at Steinastafn and *in situ* zeolites in the sea cliff at Teigarhorn (Itinerary 3).

	Surface	
Thomsonite	$NaCa_2[(Al,Si)_5O_{10}]_2 \cdot 6H_2O$	
Mesolite	$NaCa_2[Al,Si_3O_{10}]_3 \cdot 8H_2O$	TERTIARY
Scolecite	$Ca[Al_2Si_3O_{10}] \cdot 6H_2O$	BASALTS
Chabazite	$Ca[Al_2Si_4O_{12}] \cdot 6H_2O$	

Figure 8: Diagrammatic representation of zeolite zones in eastern Iceland (after Walker, 1960)

Geysers, or more properly goshvers (=gushers), are a result of the existence of large quantities of geothermally heated water in a network of cavities close to the land surface. Thorkelsson (in Barth, 1950) suggests that the spouting of these is due to reduction of pressure rather than to higher temperatures. The dissolved gases in the water are released in the form of bubbles as it rises through the crust. The bubbles become saturated with water vapour and when the water temperature approaches boiling point, the proportion of water vapour becomes very high and some of the resulting foam overflows at the surface. This so relieves the pressure on the heated water at the base of the pipe that it 'flashes' into a vast volume of spray which surges up the pipe to form a spout. See Hveragerdi, Itinerary 1 and Geysir, Itinerary 12.

Iceland

There are many locations where hot water, with temperatures below boiling point, comes close to the land surface without forming gushers e.g. Storagjá., Itinerary 5 and Landmannalaugar, Itinerary 14. Much of this is utilised to provide a cheap source of domestic hot water or to generate electricity. See Krafla power station, Itinerary 5.

ICE-RELATED FEATURES

The major phenomenon in Iceland is the *ice sheet* or ice cap. There are many of these, if all the small ones are included. They are areas of ice which do not melt in the summer and which normally occupy the highest ground. The 1:500,000 touring map recognises 17 of these, but easily the most important is the 8,300km^2 Vatnajökull, which represents 70% of all the country's ice cover and which is the third largest area of ice in the world. The ice sheets and their associated glaciers occupy about 11% (11,200km^2) of Iceland. They are formed by the accumulation of snow and its subsequent compaction into ice over hundreds of years.

Glaciers are tongues or rivers of ice, which are either 'overflows' from the ice sheets or valley glaciers originating in valley head cirques. They move slowly (<2m per day maximum) seawards. All are temperate types and respond quickly to short term climatic fluctuation.

The ice-covered area is currently much less than during the maximum of the Pleistocene glaciation, when virtually the whole country was covered. Results of the melting of the ice cover since *c*.8000 BC (10,000 B.P.) include (a) the isostatic* recovery of the landmass, resulting in a general elevation which still continues and which has caused the extensive *raised beaches** and the emergence of beds containing marine fossils in some places and (b) the deposition of numerous *morainic deposits* around the ice margins and particularly at the downstream (snout) ends of active glaciers. These terminal moraines mark periods of still-stand by the glacier as it was melting back. See Skaftafellsjökull, Itinerary 3.

As a result of ice melt in the vicinity of active volcanoes, large volumes of water are occasionally released as ice-impounded lakes overflow their dams. This results in *jökulhlaups* (Thorarinsson, 1957), which are massive water surges across adjacent valleys or coastal plains. They cause damage to roads and property in their path and have, over the post-Pleistocene period, altered parts of the landscape, mainly by building the coastal outwash plain outwards and forming *coastal sandurs*. See Myrdalsjökull, Itinerary 2.

The term *sandur* may be applied to any area of predominantly stony and inhospitable land. Essentially, there are three types (a) coastal sandurs as described above (b) valley sandurs, much the same, but confined between well-defined valley sides and (c) upland sandurs, covering large plateau areas in the interior. The last are usually snow covered in winter and have a stony surface, from which all the silts and clays (=fines) have been removed by strong winds. See Sprengisandur, Itinerary 14.

Other ice-related features include *cirques* *, *roches moutonées* *, often with *striations, eskers* *, *drumlins* *, and the abandoned shoreline marks of ice-impounded *pro-glacial lakes*, together with their *overflow channels*.

STRUCTURAL FEATURES

In areas of crustal tension such as Iceland, grabens are likely to be common features. While they are not as deep or wide as some in other parts of the world, they are vivid indications of tectonic forces at work. As the two oceanic crustal plates (American and Eurasian) are pulled apart, normal (tensional) faults develop at the margins of the zone under stress, allowing the central area to subside and also providing pathways for the ascent of magma (Figure 3; see Thingvellir, Itinerary 12).

Iceland

ITINERARIES

The itineraries which follow are divided into sequences of sites which may reasonably be completed in one day by a group with its own adequate transport. Sleeping bag accommodation and camp sites known to the authors or their advisers are mentioned as appropriate. The complete tour may be accomplished in a three week visit, but it is recommended that those who follow this guide should select the itineraries which fit their plans, depending on the time and transport they have at their disposal (Figure 9).

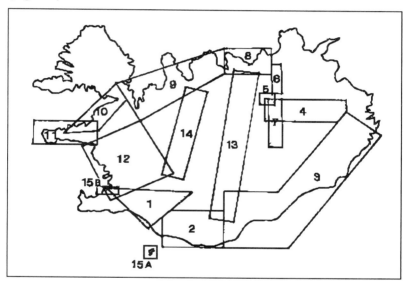

Figure 9: Itineraries.

This guide does not include all the sites of geological interest in Iceland, but instead it provides a representative selection of such sites for the interested visitor.

Michael Bamlett and John F. Potter

ITINERARY 1

The southwestern area, including Hekla

This route is based on spending the previous night in Reykjavik, allowing a start at or before 10.00 a.m. Leave the city on Highway (henceforward Hy.) 1, travelling east-southeast and following signs towards Selfoss. About 9 km from central Reykjavik, on the right and between the road and the lake (Ellidavatn), lie a group of rootless craters, RAUDHOLAR (the red hills). The cindery material from here was quarried to produce aggregate for the runways at Reykjavik airport. The craters should be noted from the vehicles, as much better, unspoiled examples occur elsewhere.

10 km further on, Hy. 417 on the south (right) leads to the Bláfjoll hills, an example of moberg. Again these features should be noted from the vehicles.

6 km further on Hy.1 the SVEINAHRAUN, a fourteenth century lava field, can be seen on the northeast side of the road and beyond it, towards the peak of Hengill (803 m), the main rift valley of the western active zone which contains the lake of Thingvallavatan (see Thingvellir, Itinerary 12).

29 km from Reykjavik centre, Hy.39 should be taken to the south. Some 12 km along this road at a point where the sea first comes into view (there is no notice or other indication) there is a major lava tube or cave on the left (northeast) side of the road. This is RAUFARHOLSHELLIR, which is in the pahoehoe (helluhraun) lava field east of Krossfjall. This tube is almost 1 km long and 3 to 4 m high. The roof has fallen in several places and great care should be taken if descending into accessible sections. Examination of the roof with the aid of a torch will reveal icicle-like lavatites, which should not be touched as they are protected by conservation law (Wood, 1971).

Continue down the old relict sea cliff on to the raised beach level to the crossroads (Hys. 38, 39 and 42) and turn left on to Hy.38. In the old cliff, which extends along much of this section of the south coast, cross-bedded lava deltas containing fragments (and occasional complete examples) of pillows may be seen from the vehicles. At the top of the lava succession, subaerial lavas act as a cap and in one case such a lava can be seen draped down the face of the cliff (Figure 10).

Hy.38 joins Hy.1 at Hveragerdi. If time allows, pay a visit to the 'geothermal' greenhouses (40% of all such in the country) where the natural heat enables sub-tropical fruit to be cultivated. The gusher named Gryta (Gryla in some versions) spouts occasionally and there are many other hot springs in and around the town which have been harnessed for

Iceland

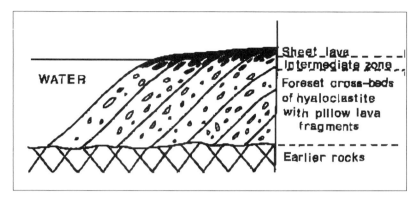

Figure 10: Lava delta and flow-foot breccia (after Jones, 1969).

domestic hot water. The steel distribution pipe for this may be seen alongside the road to the east.

Continue on Hy.1 through Selfoss, towards Hella, but turn right (southwest) on to Hy.302 just before the bridge over the melt-water river Thjorsá, which is the longest in Iceland (230 km). Leave the transport at URRIDAFOSS farm and walk east for 50-60 metres to the falls of the same name. Here, between the two active tectonic zones the river cuts pre-glacial lavas. The fall is caused partly by basic dykes cutting obliquely across the river's course.

Retrace to Hy.1 and return 2 km to the northwest before taking a right turn on to Hy.30 alongside the broad channel of the Thjorsá. Sedimentologists may wish to examine the braided features of this river's constantly shifting levées and point bars. The road runs across the Thjorsahraun lava, part of a series of 11 flows dating from around 6000 BC and covering $c.9000$ km^2. They were extruded from the Tungna volcanic field in the eastern rift zone (Jakobsson, 1976).

5 km beyond Brautarholt (which has sleeping bag accommodation and a geothermally heated swimming pool) turn right (east) on to Hy.32, continuing alongside the Thjorsá for about 30 km, before turning left on to the un-numbered road to STÖNG, beside an east side tributary of the river Fossá. At Stöng there is an excavated and preserved farmhouse, one of many in this area which were probably partly buried by the pumice fall from Hekla in 1104 A.D. (Figure 11). The resulting poor crops led to the local population moving out over the ensuing years. A board reveals the latest information about excavations.

Michael Bamlett and John F. Potter

To the southwest there is another group of rootless craters along the Fossá valley. Beyond these is the rhyolitic moberg of RAUDUKAMBAR. A rough 2 hour (each way) walk up the Fossá valley (about 16 km round trip) reaches Iceland's second highest waterfall HAIFOSS (122 m).

Return to Hy.32 and turn left, passing the replica of the medieval turf-roofed farmhouse THJODVELDISBAERINN, built in 1974 to commemorate 1100 years of settlement in Iceland. The road follows the Thjorsá and climbs above the Burfell hydro-electric power plant (commissioned 1969; 210,000 kw). Burfell and the adjacent Skeljafell are inliers of Tertiary lavas which are completely surrounded by later, post-glacial TUNGNARHRAUN lavas.

Light vehicles may be able to cross the Thjorsá at the ice-floe trap above the power station tunnel, but coaches must continue a further 12 km or so to the main bridge. Some 3 km beyond this, turn sharply to the right (westwards) on to Hy.26, which follows the left bank of the Thjorsá back towards Burfell. Follow this road for *c.* 14 km to the Burfell airstrip on the right. Opposite this, take the un-numbered track eastwards for about 12 km towards Landmannalaugar (see Itinerary 14). Light vehicles may be able to continue to there, but coaches are recommended to follow the route below.

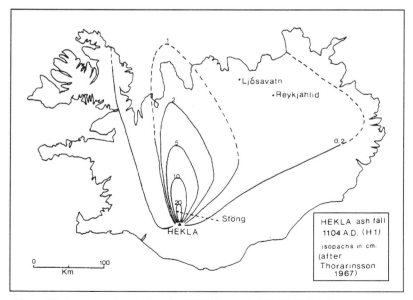

Figure 11: Isopachs (in cm) for the H1 Hekla ash fall of 1104 A.D.

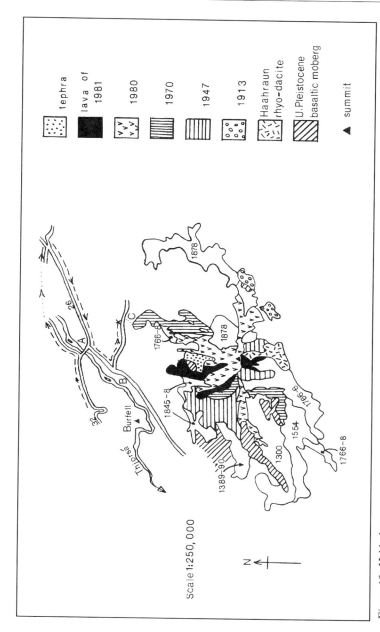

Figure 12: Hekla lavas.

Michael Bamlett and John F. Potter

The 1970 basaltic aa lava from Hekla will be seen as a black-on-grey feature about 600 m from the track, on its right hand side (south). High clearance vehicles can approach the lava front, but others should remain on the track. The flow front, with its blocky aa-type features should be approached on foot (Gronvold et al, 1983).

Hekla has erupted frequently during post-glacial times and has produced rocks of a variety of compositions between rhyolitic and basaltic (Figures 11 and 12 and Table 1).

TABLE 1	*Post-glacial ash falls from Hekla*	
	H1	1104 AD (2 km^3 of rhyolitic ash)
	H3	2800-2900 BP
	H2	$c.3500$ BP (The Selsund pumice)
	H4	4000-4500 BP
	H5	6200-6700 BP

Note The H numbers are in the order given, having once been dated differently.

On January 17 1991, Hekla erupted again. After 10 minutes, radar monitors detected a plume of smoke and ash 11.5 km high. Several fissures were active to start with, but activity soon settled at one fissure on the lower southern flank and continued until 11 March. 0.15 km^3 of fresh lava covered 23 km^2 and the uncompressed tephra amounted to 0.02 km^3. The lava composition was similar to that of the eruptions of 1981 (0.15 km^3 of lava) and 1970 (0.20 km^3 lava). The highest effusion rate was reached during the initial 9 hours when 2000 m^3 of lava per second were produced. However, the average rate for most of the period was 1 m^3 per second.

Retrace to Hy.26 and turn left, following this road southwestwards to join Hy.1 at VEGAMOR, then turn left towards Hella, where it is possible to stay overnight in sleeping bag accommodation or on one of the two camp sites. There is also sleeping bag accommodation at Heimaland or, for the more adventurous, two camp sites and two mountain huts at the head of the Thorsmork valley. Itinerary 2 includes descriptions of localities adjacent to the Thorsmork sites.

Iceland

ITINERARY 2

South Central coastal area, Hella to Hof, including Thorsmork

Leaving Hella on Hy.1, pass through Hvolsvöllur and 8 km further on, fork left on to Hy.249/250 after crossing the Affall river. A new (1992) section of road carries Hy.1 eastwards over the Markafljót river.

After crossing this on Hy.250, note the isolated moberg hill, Stora Dimon, on the left and the ice cap of Eyjafjallajökull in front. There are many deep fords on this road so it is not recommended for vehicles with low clearances. About 17 km after leaving Hy.1, a short deviation to the south of the main valley road reaches the snout of GIGJÖKULL , a glacier flowing northwards from Eyjafjallajökull (see back cover). The proglacial lake, trapped behind a terminal moraine, often has ice floes on it. The volcano under the Eyjafjallajökull ice last erupted in 1821-22.

5 km further east along the valley is the boulder field (some boulders are up to 3 m in diameter) which resulted from a rock slide on the Steinholtsjökull glacier in January 1967. A glacial lake overflowed northwards into the main valley, carrying the boulders and a large volume of smaller material.

A short way beyond the boulder field is the south side tributary ravine of STOKKHOLTSGJÁ. At least one hour should be allowed for the exploration of this feature on foot. Cross-bedded hyaloclastites are present on the left (north) side, with isolated basaltic pillows (<0.5 m diameter). See Figure 10; Jones (1969). Yellow to pale green olivine crystals are present in the basalts. At the confluence of the two tributary streams in the ravine, take the left hand branch and continue until the valley sides close in even further. A short scramble provides a view of a thin meltwater fall from the glacier.

Approaching the head of the Thorsmork valley there is a choice of camp site/mountain hut accommodation. The easier, but less interesting is on the south side of the valley at GODALAND, while that on the north side involves the often difficult fording of the Krossá river (see back cover). The valley contains a constantly changing braided stream pattern and in late spring and early summer is often impossible to cross. Complex ripple patterns in water-deposited ash may be noted in abandoned channels (Bluck, 1974). If time allows, the ascent of the hill behind this northern camp site gives good views of the moberg hills of the THRONGÁ valley to the north and there are some good periglacial stone stripes, now vegetated, on the slope.

If it should prove possible to return along the north side of the

Thorsmork valley, a route which is only accessible to 4-wheel drive vehicles and walkers, visits should be made to the outcrops of the interglacial Thorsmork ignimbrite east of TROLLABUDIR. This was deposited when the Tindafjallajökull caldera collapsed (Thorarinsson, 1969a).

Most groups will retrace to the Hy.1/Hy.249 junction and then proceed eastwards on Hy.1. Soon after the road junction, the water supply pipe to the Westmann Islands can be seen crossing beneath the road (see Itinerary 15 A).

About 5 km southwards from the road junction, the 60 m high waterfall SELJALANDSFOSS, descends the former sea cliff to road level. It is possible to walk behind the fall, where there are several lavas and a good mud/rubble diamictite* (Sigvalda & Bergh, 1991). In the southern wall of the embayment containing the fall, at the top of the grass slope, the lower glassy contact of a columnar jointed olivine basalt can be examined.

4 km further on is HEIMALAND, where there is sleeping bag accommodation in the school. Good views of the Westmann Islands may be had from this area in clear weather. 23 km beyond Heimaland is another fall, SKOGAFOSS (61 m), which is visible on the left hand side of the road. Early Icelandic dwellings and a museum of contemporary artefacts may be viewed at the Skogar museum and there is an Edda Hotel here also.

6 km further on Hy.1, a track on the left leads 5 km northwards across the Skogar sandur, much of which was deposited by a jökulhlaup in c.800 A.D., to the snout of SOLHEIMAJÖKULL glacier. The glacier is about 10 km long, extending southwards from the Myrdalsjökull ice cap. In general, the snout is receding, but occasional surges mean that since 1985 the track along the ice front has been blocked by a substantial advance of terminal moraine material. Full exploration of the ice margin requires wellington boots.

After examining the frequently changing glacial phenomena here return to Hy.1 and continue towards VIK. A short (5 km each way) deviation may be made along Hy.218 to the most southerly point of the mainland at DYRHÓLAEY (=headland with a door or, indeed, Portland!). A large arch through the basaltic moberg is complemented by several stacks offshore.

At Vik, there are exposures immediately east of the town and also to the southwest, below Reyniafjall, which demonstrate Surtseyan activity. Thin beds of water-laid tuff contain broken fragments of earlier pillow lava, some of which lie in shallow sag structures*. The headland to the southwest has some columnar basalts and the adjacent, jökulhlaup-deposited shoreline is now being rapidly eroded by the sea.

Iceland

Drive across the Myrdalssandur, a low, flat gravel deposit, which owes its existence to jökulhlaups generated by eruptions of KATLA which lies beneath the Myrdalsjökull ice. Since 1300, the coast has advanced more than 3 km. The latest major advance occurred in 1918, when a major addition to the sandur was made in the form of the Vik deposit (Jonsson, 1982). The highway authorities delayed the building of a metalled road across this section of Hy.1 as another major jökulhlaup was anticipated. So far (1992) it has not occurred and the road has now been built.

In the area of HERJOLFSSTADIR there is a widely scattered group of small, rootless craters. The opportunity should be taken to examine the well-exposed and structureless internal arrangement of these features. North of the junction with Hy.211 and the bridge over the Holmsá river, some 12 km northwards, there are numerous piles of stones (cairns) adjacent to the road. At the Holmsá crossing there are two bridges; the southerly one over the Holmsá and the northern one over one of its tributaries. In the western bank of the main Holmsá are poor pillow lavas of late Pleistocene age, overlain by lavas from the southwestern continuation of the Eldgjá fissure, locally termed the Holmshraun and dated at 934 A.D. (2 on Figure 13). These lavas form columnar structures on the east bank of the river downstream from the bridge (3).

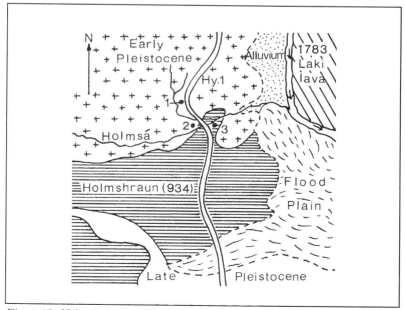

Figure 13: Holmsá crossing area. (1 – fuel station).

Michael Bamlett and John F. Potter

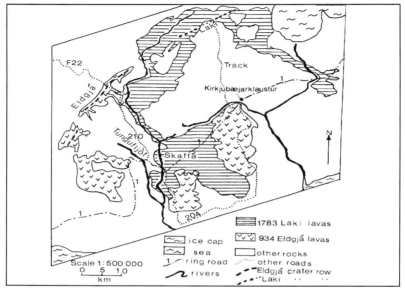

Figure 14: Eldgjá and Laki lava fields

Continue northwards on Hy.1 to TUNGUSEL, where there is a community centre (and nothing else!), which is a possible overnight stop (sleeping bag accommodation). Other possibilities are to be found at Landmannalaugar (camp sites and mountain hut) (Itinerary 14) and at Kirkjubaejarklaustur or Hof (sleeping bag accommodation).

A kilometre beyond Tungusel is a bridge over the Kúdafljót river and a road junction with Hy.208, which marks the conclusion of this section. Continue now to Itinerary 3 (the southeast) or 14 (the Sprengisandur, in reverse)

ITINERARY 3

The southeast, Tungusel to Egilsstadir, including Laki

From the Kúdafljót bridge, drive along Hy.1 for *c*.5 km to the junction with Hy.204 at Asar, where a metalled section of the main road begins. This crosses the SKAFTARELDAHRAUN formed of distinctive lavas which flowed from the Laki fissure in 1783-4 and covered 556 km^2, the greatest single effusion of lava ever witnessed by humans. These lavas covered much of the area adjacent to the fissure before overflowing along the Skaftá valley and spreading out across the coastal lowland now traversed by Hy.1. There

Iceland

they rest on top of the Eldgjá lavas of 934 A.D. (Figure 14), which had come the same way (see Itinerary 14).

As a result of the later event some 20 farms were abandoned and a period of sickness and famine ensued (the Moduhardindi), during which over 9000 people died. It is reported by contemporary observers that a blue haze covered the area during the summer of 1783. This was probably rich in fluorine and sulphur dioxide, which poisoned a large proportion of cattle, ponies and sheep. Inevitably, famine followed and 20% of the population of remote rural areas died of hunger. The haze cloud, in a diluted form, extended over parts of northern Europe as far as the Altai Mountains in Siberia (Sigurdsson, 1982; Sigvaldason & Oskarsson, 1986).

Hy.1 crosses the lava field for 18 km. At the eastern end of the section, the 45 km long track northwards to LAKI leaves the main road, which continues over the southern margins of the Eldgjá lava for a further 6 km to KIRKJUBAEJARKLAUSTUR. This could be a convenient overnight stop if a visit to Laki is planned.

Less than 1 km along the Hy.203 from the crossroads at the Skaftá river crossing is the KIRKUGOLF (=church floor). This is a remarkably symmetrical set of basalt columns in the Pleistocene lavas. They are part of a small conservation area and SHOULD NOT BE HAMMERED.

Laki (by R. Toynton)

See Figure 14.

A high clearance vehicle with 4-wheel drive is strongly recommended for this section, as there are numerous fords and the road is often muddy.

Almost immediately after leaving Hy.1, cross the Skaftá river and the Skaftareldahraun is replaced by the greater relief of hyaloclastite outcrops. In this area the landscape is usually green with a relatively high population of sheep. There is clear evidence of soil erosion due to overgrazing.

Where the road swings right across the GEIRLANDSÁ river, leave the vehicles and walk 100 m down the west bank of the river to the FAGRIFOSS waterfall and viewpoint. Downstream can be seen two dykes breached by the river which, due to differential erosion, stand proud from the valley floor by some 7 m. They are oriented northeast to southwest parallel to the Laki fissure (see above).

As the road climbs into the more barren area towards the summit at GALTI, glimpses of Sidujökull, a broad outlet glacier from the Vatnajökull ice cap can be seen to the northeast. On the Galti summit, well-winnowed ash covers the ground surface. From this point, the line of the Laki fissure

Michael Bamlett and John F. Potter

can be picked out as a series of pale grey and pink cones in the middle distance, with the higher peaks of Graenifjallgardur and Fogrufjöll behind. Ahead, the road descends into the upper Skaftá valley.

The road now follows the southeastern boundary of the blocky Skaftareldhraun lava and the going becomes more difficult, before turning northwards and terminating on the lower slopes of LAKI MOUNTAIN. The crater row formed by the Laki fissure is 25 km long and contains more than 100 craters (Thorarinsson, 1969b), though at almost its mid-point it is interrupted by the pre-existing Laki mountain (818 m).

The easy ascent of the cinder cone immediately next to the road is rewarded by a remarkable view to the southwest. The Skaftareldahraun fills the valley, with its margins clearly visible. Down the centre of the valley, leading away from the cone on which you stand, the line of the fissure is picked out by light grey scoria linking a string of cones of various sizes. On either side, equidistant from the fissure line and gently rising and falling along the valley sides, is a pair of parallel normal faults. They are clearly discernable in the relief, resulting in a graben feature which contains the fissure and the lava. On turning to view the northeast, the line of fissures and cones dies out on the lower slopes of Laki mountain, but the subsidence structure continues, with the fault on the southeast of the fissure passing close to the summit. The faults and fissure re-emerge on the opposite side of the mountain.

Descending into the centre of the cinder cone, it is possible to enter a small volcanic pipe, the walls of which are covered with spatter type material, and to look upwards through a collapsed section to open sky. An exploration of the area within a few hundred metres of the road reveals several cones of various sizes which can be entered. There is also a fine, winding lava tube, the roof of which has almost completely collapsed.

Unfortunately, the time taken to reach Laki limits the time available for exploration. As there is no other road, the return journey must be back to Hy.1 by the same route.

From Kirkjubaejarklaustur eastwards, the metalled Hy.1 runs across the alluvium of the Skaftá estuary. Between Horgsland and Foss (both are farms) the road runs beneath hyaloclastite cliffs which mark the margin of the Pleistocene lavas. At Foss, the road ascends the lavas and a stop should be made at the DVERGHAMRAR conservation area, south of the road (see Figure 7). The entrance is marked by an information board. There are some basaltic columns here, with well-defined chisel marks. It is clear that the basalts were erupted beneath a layer of tephra.

About 2 km beyond Dverghamrar lies the eastern branch of the

Iceland

Skaftareldahraun lavas of 1783 (see Figure 13), locally termed the BRUNAHRAUN (=burning lava). This branch followed the Hverfisfljót river valley and ran through Pleistocene hyaloclastites before spreading out on to the Brunasandur alluvium. The road passes on to the post-glacial NUPAHRAUN lava for about 5 km as far as KALAFELL. This flow has its origins beneath the Sidujökull lobe of the Vatnajökull ice cap.

The VATNAJÖKULL ICE CAP now dominates the landscape ahead and the road crosses the SKEIDARARSANDUR, with its innumerable meltwater streams. This section of road was the final link in the Ring Road (Hy.1) and was completed in 1974, with the construction of the bridges over the Nupsvötn, Sandgygjukvisl and Skeidará rivers.

It is not usually worth stopping in this section, but the following should be observed in passing:

- The huge spur cliff at Lomagnupur, rising precipitously from sea-level to 767m in only 2000 m horizontal distance.

- The longest bridge in Iceland over the Skeidará (994 m).

- Isolated nineteenth century terminal moraines of the Skeidararjökull north of the road.

- Views of glaciers spilling from the west side of the Oraefajökull lobe of the Vatnajökull. This section includes the highest point in Iceland at 2119 m. The Öraefajökull central volcano lies outside the eastern active zone and its two most recent eruptions were in 1362 and 1717 A.D. To the north-northwest, however the Grimsvötn volcano has occasionally produced powerful jökulhlaups which have affected this area of the south coast. In 1934, the Skeidará became 9 km wide and the flow rate was estimated at 64,000 m^3/sec. The latest major flood here was in 1972.

At the eastern end of the road across the Skeidararsandur is the Skaftafell campsite. It is worth stopping here for refreshment or, if camping, for an overnight stay. Booking is advised in the high season. There are at least two walks of geological interest, both well trodden and sign-posted. It may not be possible to include both unless you are staying on the site or in the community hall at HOF, 23 km further to the southeast (See Figure 15).

Walk 1

Allow between one and two hours depending on the mobility of party. Follow the signposts "Svartifoss" to the north-northwest of the camp site. The path soon begins to climb the abandoned cliff line and after 1.5 km emerges at a viewpoint looking upstream along the BARAGIL VALLEY towards the SVARTIFOSS waterfall, in columnar jointed Tertiary basalts.

Michael Bamlett and John F. Potter

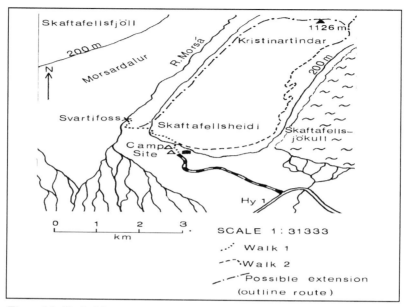

Figure 15: Skaftafell area.

The scramble down into the gorge for a close-up view of the fall will add an extra hour to the walk. Return to the camp site the same way.

Walk 2

Allow at least 2 hours, depending how far you wish to walk along the track. Follow the "Svartifoss" signs as in Walk 1 until a few metres after the start of the climb from the edge of the camp site. Here, another path signposted "Austurbreikur" goes off to the right. This is a steeper and, at first, rougher climb than the Svartifoss path.

After some 40-50 minutes steady walking, the Skaftafellsjökull glacier can be viewed from above. The layout of the abandoned terminal moraines and the outwash plain* to the south can also be seen. The few rock outcrops adjacent to the path are in Upper Pleistocene basic hyaloclastites and tuffs, but the top of the sequence here is a small rhyolite outcrop at the summit of the inter-stream area. Either return the same way or, for those with a whole day to spend here, it is possible to walk across the KRISTINARTINDAR to Svartifoss or to continue up to the edge of the Vatnajökull ice, a return trip of about 22 km.

The next section of 55 km along the Hy.1 through HOF (where there is

Iceland

a farm, GROF, which has been excavated in the ash fall of 1362 from Öraefajökull) is dominated by views of the Vatnajökull ice sheet to the north. Its glaciers approach the road in several places. Examples are at KVIARJÖKULL and FJALLSJÖKULL. At the latter, it is possible to view the ice front some 200 m from the road and a stop may be considered worthwhile.

Between here and JÖKULSARLÓN, a long terminal moraine runs parallel to the road on its northern side, and at Jökulsarlón it impounds a pro-glacial lake. There are usually many ice fragments in this lagoon and, in the tourist season, it is possible to arrange boat trips among these. Over the succeeding 66 km there is little worth a stop but the following should be noted in passing:

- The 789 m - high cliff of STEINFJALL, in Tertiary basalts (14 km from Jökulsarlón).

- The small, 1000 kw output hydro-electric power station at SMYRLABORG, built in 1969 (33 km).

- The numerous longshore bars built by tidal currents, flowing from west to east in most cases.

- The bridge, built in 1961, 225 m long, over the constriction in the course of the HORNAFJARDARFLJÓT, with braided river features both above and below it.

- The further glaciers and ice front of VATNAJÖKULL to the north.

Where Hy.1 turns southwards, about 64 km from Jökulsarlón, note the hill on the east side of the road, KETILLAUGARFJALL (668 m). This is mainly a late Tertiary gabbro intrusion, flanked by rhyolitic ring dykes and associated with a subsidence caldera.

HÖFN is a town of about 1700 people and has an hotel, a camp site and sleeping bag accommodation. There is a geothermally-heated swimming pool. In clear weather there are magnificent views southwestwards towards Öraefajökull, which include several glaciers.

The geology of the east of Iceland is dominated by Tertiary age basalts. There are no active volcanoes or ice sheets. There is, however, plenty to interest the visiting geologist.

In a direct line, some 12-13 km east of Höfn lie the twin headlands of STOKKSNES and VESTURHORN. These prominences are formed by a gabbroic intrusion which has deformed the lavas on the landward side, where there is also a (later) acid intrusion. The road follows the col between

Michael Bamlett and John F. Potter

these two intrusions on the one side and the Tertiary lavas of SKALATINDUR on the other. The full explanation of the origin and character of these intrusions awaits detailed geochemical studies. A similar problem applies to the microgranite intrusion into the Tertiary basalts which outcrops in the first valley after the col on the left (north). While this may be associated with the acid intrusion noted above, it is marked on the geological map as 'microgranite' and is the only such designation in Iceland. The location of this outcrop, which is easily seen with binoculars from the road, is known as SCAUFRUDAL in the valley of ENDALAUSIDALUR.

About 19 km beyond the Endalausidalur bridge, near HILD, outcrops of rhyolite and granophyre* may be seen in a roadside (north) exposure. These are related to the Lön Tertiary central volcano, which was basaltic in its activity until the post-caldera rejuvenation phase, which produced these acid lavas and intrusions. Further proof of this activity can be seen about 16 km further on immediately after rounding the Austurhorn headland. On the landward side of the road, in a scattered series of outcrops, is a net-vein complex, south of the HVALDALSÁ bridge. It is clear from the chilled margins of the pale granophyre that it was the intrusive rock (Holmes, 1965, p.266).

There follows a series of fjords, around which the road normally hugs the shoreline. These landforms, mostly in Tertiary basalts, are more deeply eroded than the younger lavas of the active zone and form valleys which were sufficiently deep to be (a) filled with glacier ice during the Pleistocene and (b) 'drowned' when the sea-level rose when the overall ice cover melted. Also, this marginal land area is not subject to the tectonic uplift of the modern active zone.

The first of the eastern fjords is ALFTAFJÖRDUR, which is almost totally enclosed by a sand bar. On turning into the succeeding HAMARSFJÖRDUR, clear weather gives a good view of a wide cirque* on the eastern flank of KAMBFELL (1109 m). On the north side of this fjord lies the red intrusive mass of BULANDSTINDUR (1069 m) which is, in turn, intruded by several basic dykes, one of which just east of the main mass of red rocks, stands separate and proud of the main topography to the south of the road. There are others in the cliff all along this section.

DJÚPIVOGUR is a village at the outer end of Hamarsfjördur and offers an hotel, toilets and refreshment facilities. Near the entrance to BERUFJÖRDUR at the top of a gentle rise through a shallow road cutting, on the right (south) of the road, is the farm of TEIGAHORN. Here, there is an unusual example of geological conservation. The land holder is charged with making sure that the remarkable coastal section, which

Iceland

contains Tertiary vesicular basalts incorporating 10-12 varieties of zeolites, is not spoiled by mineral collectors. In return, he is allowed to extract and to sell a limited number of specimens from the site. Ask at the newer farm building where permission is usually given. It is best to avoid meal times if possible. Leave all hammers in your vehicle; reasonably priced specimens are on sale in the makeshift shop to which your guide will direct you after visiting the site.

There are further, less well developed zeolites in the roadstone quarry at the head of the fjörd, just east of the junction with Hy.939. About 17 km from this junction, between the road and the shore is an accessible outcrop of one of the ignimbrites* from the Tertiary central volcano of BREIDALUR (Breidafell) (Walker, 1963). The presence of numerous dykes allied to pyroclastic deposits in this area are indications of a major volcanic vent. It is thought to lie to the northwest of Breidalur, the next valley to the north. The ignimbrite here is a pale, grey-green colour and comprises explosion debris, including fiamme* of flattened pumice. It may be traced up the adjacent hillside between the lavas, with which it is conformable (Cas & Wright, 1987, p.224; Sparks *et al.*, 1981).

Follow Hy.1 along the coast for a further 18 km and, just beyond the place where the road turns towards the northwest at STREITISHVARF headland, park on the northeast side of the road. A walk of *c*. 500 m parallel to the shore towards the northwest reaches a major composite dyke, about 25 m wide. There are dark, outer basaltic sections (1 on Figure 16), each 4-5 m thick and a central, pale brown to white, felsitic, quartz-phyric core (2), which contains partly digested fragments of the outer (and therefore earlier) basic rocks. The sea has broken through the seaward basaltic wall and eroded away much of the less resistent felsite. In clear weather the continuation of the feature can be seen in the upper section of the cliff to the north-northeast, on the opposite side of Breidalsvik inlet. It continues northwards for about 30 km.

NOTE: If time is short, it is possible to omit the next section and to proceed directly to EGILSSTADIR on Hy.1 or to the sleeping bag accommodation at HALLBJARNSSTADIR, alongside LAGARFLJÖT via Hy.931.

Michael Bamlett and John F. Potter

Figure 16: Composite dyke at Breidalsvik (sketch from photograph).
(See front cover)

24 km after leaving Hy.1 for Hy.96 at the head of the Breidalsvik inlet
(Heydalir), the village of STODVAFJÖRDUR (on the fjörd of the same
name) is reached. In a cottage and its garden on the landward side of the
road (STEINASTAFN) is a collection of rocks and minerals mainly from
the eastern fjörds area. Zeolites, chalcedony, obsidian and various coloured
cherts dominate the display, for which a small viewing charge is made.

About 28 km further on, on the north side of FASKRUDSFJÖRDUR,
clear weather will permit a view of the laccolith* on SANDFELL on the
southern side of the fjörd (Figure 17). The succeeding 50 km passes the
headland of HAFNARNES and then along the south side of
REYDARFJÖRDUR, at 30 km the longest of the eastern fjörds.
Approaching the end of the fjörd, note views across to the town of
BUDAREYRI (or Reydarfjördur). Near here, at HEUGUSTADIR were
workings yielding calcite ("Iceland spar") for microscope lenses. There are
(1991) plans to build an aluminium smelter on the north bank of the fjörd.
A small section of coastal bars and lagoons may be seen adjacent to the
road 3.5 km before the junction with Hy.92. Either continue to
ESKIFJÖRDUR for accommodation or take Hy.92 northwards across the
FAGRIDALUR pass to EGILSSTADIR and rejoin Hy.1. Note in passing
the numerous earthy-looking red boles* between lava flows, indicative of
subaerial weathering and possible soil formation (paleosols).

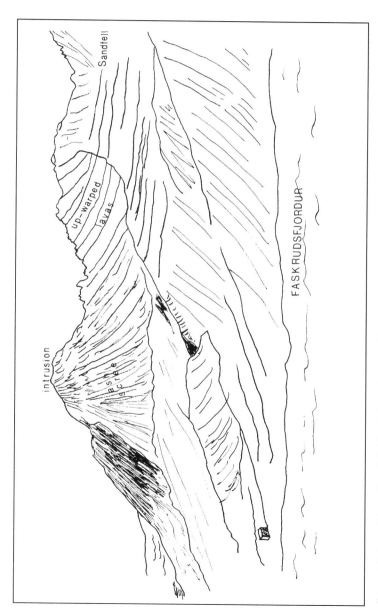

Figure 17: Laccolith on Sandfell (sketch from photograph).

Michael Bamlett and John F. Potter

ITINERARY 4

Egilsstadir to Reykjahlid (Myvatn)

Leaving Egilsstadir on Hy.1 and travelling northwards, the geothermal source for the town's hot water since 1979 is passed, just north of the junction with Hy.925. Cold water from a small lake (URRIDAVATN) is conducted down boreholes to a relict heat source in Tertiary lavas and pumped up at 120°C. Extensive areas of roches moutonées* can be seen east of the road. In ditches alongside the road, a layer of pale pumiceous ash contains tephra from the 1875 fissure eruption north of ASKJA. A twisting descent precedes the bridge over the JOKULSÁ Á BRÚ, beyond which is an isolated but popular and comfortable purpose-built sleeping bag hostel at BRUARAS. Turn left at the top of the hill and continue southwestwards along the left bank of the Jokulsá á Brú, noting the extensive morainic deposits on both sides of the valley. 28 km from Bruaras a tributary stream joins the main river as a waterfall – RJUKANDI (or Fjallfoss). Below the fall there are two red boles – one behind the lower section of the fall and the other near the road and more easily accessible. The lava base above the latter is vesicular, probably due to water in the soil vapourising as it was engulfed by the flow.

A further 6 km to the south, Hy.1 leaves the Jökuldalur to traverse the JOKULSDALHEIDI plateau. In clear weather the strato-volcano of SNAEFELL (1833 m) stands out to the south near the northern edge of Vatnajökull. The lava over which the road runs now becomes younger as the active zone is approached again. If the visibility is good, it is worth stopping at the top of the hill above the JOKULSÁ Á FJÖLLUM valley near the eastern edge of the active zone. Make the ascent of the hill to the south of the road at a point just east of SLORFELL (844 m). Although this hill partly blocks the view it is possible to see across the valley to the southwest, HERDUBREID (a tuya) with its small ice cap topping the subaerial lava. Beyond that is the DYNGJUFJÖLL caldera at Askja and the shield volcano of KOLLÓTTADYNGA (1180 m). The parallel north-northeast to south-southwest rows of craters marking the eastward movement of the volcanic zone during the Pleistocene can be seen alongside the Jokulsá. Return to the vehicles and descend the hill to MODRUDALUR where there is a cafe, toilets and fuel station. Alongside the road here there are numerous kettle holes*. From here, it is possible to gain access to the ASKJA area via the F 98 track (see Itinerary 7).

About 16 km north from Modrudalur, on the west (left) side of the road, at VLIDIDALUR, a cone shows red oxidised scoria*, indicating subaerial eruptive activity during an interglacial period. This is unusual, as most of the craters in this area are of subaqueous hyaloclastites.

Figure 18: Soil pillar by roadside, north of Modrudalur (sketch from photograph).

Michael Bamlett and John F. Potter

About 4 km further on (20 km from Modrudalur) on the right (east) of the road, erosion has broken up the land surface into a series of soil pillars which demonstrate clearly some of the tephra layers from major eruptions, as shown in Figure 18.

The major road junction at GRIMSSTADIR has a fuel station and a camp site. Turn west, continuing on Hy.1 for 7 km then drive a short way along the F 88 track to the entrance to the Surtseyan* tuff ring of HROSSABORG. It may be possible to drive into the crater, but in recent years the track has become deeply rutted. The main constituents of the fragmental material, which forms the rim of the cone in radially outward-dipping layers, are accretionary tephra. The fragments are of various diameters, between 0.02 and 2.0 metres. They comprise a basaltic nucleus (1 on Figure 19) surrounded by hyaloclastite glass (3) containing further small basalt fragments (2), which became embedded in the glass while it was still molten.

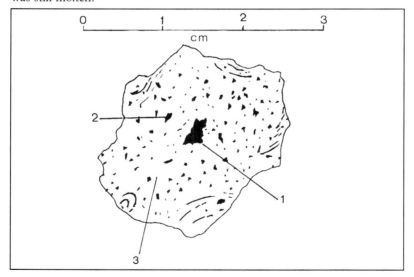

Figure 19: Cored or armoured lapillus from Hrossaborg.

Climb to the rim to examine the tephra closely, in conjunction with the stratification. In clear weather the view to the south complements the earlier one (see above p.34) of the peaks to the south towards KOLLÓTTADYNGA Take a compass and a map and try to identify those which stand out.

Iceland

Return to Hy.1 and drive 3.4 km to a small building set back from the road on the south (left). This is PETURSKIRKJE, which stands on the top of the eastern lava from the 1875 flow from a fissure north of Askja (Austura Hrauntagi), the front of which may be examined here. Continue to MYVATN where there is a wide variety of accommodation at Reykjahlid and Skutustadir. Prior booking is essential here, particularly during July and August.

ITINERARY 5

The Myvatn area

This itinerary assumes residence for 3 nights at Reykjahlid or Skutustadir. The features described are arranged in a loose order of visiting but may, of course, be taken in any convenient sequence (Figure 20). Those marked with ** in the text are regarded as the most important.

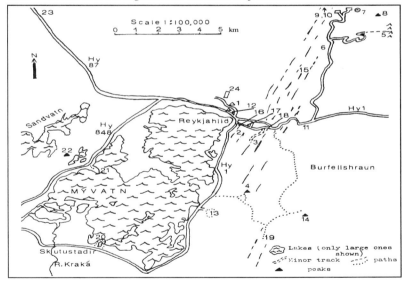

Figure 20: Myvatn and Reykjahlid area.

KEY:
1. Campsite	9. Leirnjúkur	17. Swimming pool
2. Storagjá	10. Site of 1984 eruption	18. Bjarnarflag power station
3. Grjótagjá	11. Namafjall hot springs	19. Ludentisborgir crater row
4. Hverfjall	12. Raykjahlid hotel	20. Rootless craters
5. Hraffntinnuhryggur	13. Dimmugorgir	21. Rootless craters
6. Krafla geothermal station	14. Lúdent	22. Vindbelgjarfjall (529 m)
7. Viti crater	15. Indication of regional rifting trend	23. Large terminal moraine; outwash of Holasandur
8. Krafla peak	16. "Volcano films" cinema	24. Airstrip

Michael Bamlett and John F. Potter

At SKUTUSTADIR** are the best rootless craters in Iceland. They lie on a small peninsula between the road (Hy.1) and the lake, adjacent to the camp site and the sleeping bag accommodation. The area is a Nature Reserve; no hammering or collecting is allowed and visitors should keep strictly to the marked paths and avoid disturbing the numerous birds.

DIMMUBORGIR** is a unique example of relict lava pillars. The younger Laxa lavas (dated at c.2000 BP) from the Ludentisborgir-Threndslaborgir crater row flowed westwards towards pre-historic Myvatn. At the lake margins, steam was generated by the lava-water interaction and began the process of rootless crater development. However, before the craters could form, and prior to the full solidification of the lava, the majority of the molten rock drained away, leaving a few solid pillars 10-20 m high. Some of these show crude chisel marks. There are two main features which support the above interpretation (a) the uneven, lava-smeared sides of the pillars, created as the lava pulled away from the solidified sections at the time of the drain out and (b) 'tide marks' in the form of lava rings around the pillars, which are taken to represent brief pauses during the period of lava withdrawal. The attitude of the pillars suggests that the area was slightly domed prior to the lava outflow.

About 1 km north from the side track to Dimmuborgir is a field gate marking the start of a 12 km walk which encompasses HVERFJALL (or Hverfell); part of the LÚDENTISBORGIR-THRENDSLABORGIR CRATER ROW; LÚDENT and numerous other small-scale volcanic related features. A generous half day should be allowed if the walk is to be attempted. The path begins as a rough track leading to Hverfjall, which is an explosion crater with fist-sized, cindery tephra. It evolved 2500 to 2700 years ago in a series of subaerial explosive events, evidenced by the large blocks of pre-existing solid lava which litter its slopes, especially inside the crater. A path leads up to the rim, from which all the large-scale features of the walk may be seen. A map is essential.

Descend on the southeast side of the crater and follow the track in a general southerly direction, with the row of craters on the left (east) until there is a gap through the row, adjacent to some good spatter cones. Continue to the southeast towards an eastern offset of the crater row, southwest of Lúdent. Follow the line of cones as far as required, then retrace to LÚDENT, using the path on the eastern side of the fissures. Lúdentskal crater is another explosion feature, the oldest in this area (c.9000 B.P.). On its northwest flank is an Icelandite* flow dated at 3800 B.P. which can be examined.

Walk round the lower end of the flow and continue northwards across the DRUMABAROND LAVAS for about 4 km. Poorly defined linear

Iceland

depressions in the soil are part of large 30+ m diameter ice wedge polygons.

Turn gradually towards the northwest, heading for a point on Hy.1 about 0.75 to 1.0 km west of the diatomite plant, the buildings of which are at the foot of the larger hills in front and on the right. DIATOMITE is the product of the refining of diatom tests dredged from the floor of Myvatn by suction pump. Diatoms are microscopic unicellular algae which, while they are alive, are free floating. They have siliceous tests, built by absorbing silica which occurs in solution in the water of Myvatn.

The track, which is not well marked, goes gently down the slope into a shallow graben which lies along the axis of the tectonic depression, with occasional fault scarps between 1 and 5 m in height. On the face of one of these, a base surge deposit* from an explosive eruption, has covered a pre-existing lava mound. Continue from here to the road.

Further west, close to and to the east of the junction of Hy.1 and Hy.87 in Reykjahlid, two of the graben's west side fault scarps may be examined. That at STORAGJA**, the outer and more westerly of the two, also exhibits a dilation fissure in which there is geothermally heated water (at 35°C when tested in 1986). The fault displaces lavas which pre-date the H5 Hekla ash (see Table 1). Other, younger lavas to the north and south of this are undisturbed.

About 2 km southwest from the diatomite factory, along a well marked and slightly rugged track, the lower and better marked fault scarp may be examined at GROTAGJA**. The throw of the fault here is about 4 m and behind some of the rotated blocks dilation fissures have allowed seepage of hot water into the voids. In 1986, the water temperature here was 52°C. About 100 m north of the pool, lavas from Namafjall, erupted about 2000 B.P., cover the fault scarp. Adjacent to the track and between the scarp and the main road, an iron bar has been cemented into the ground over one of the steam-emitting fissures. In 1986, this had broken and parted about 45 mm, a distance which had hardly changed by 1990. It provides a crude indication of the rate at which the two parts of Iceland- essentially the Eurasian and American tectonic plates are moving apart. The movements are also monitored much more accurately using laser equipment (Decker et al, 1976; Gerke 1974).

Turn northwards at the road junction (Hys. 1 and 87) and park in the area adjacent to the Reykjahlid Hotel. From here, take the short walk to the area around the church which is covered by the LEIRNJUKUR LAVA of 1729. Good examples of ropy lava, tumuli and collapse structures can be examined.

Michael Bamlett and John F. Potter

Continue west on Hy.87, then turn south on to Hy.848 to a group of craters on the peninsula of VINDBELGUR, about 5.5 km south of the 87/848 junction and below the Pleistocene moberg hill of VINDBELGJARFJALL. This is a conservation area of considerable importance to ornithologists. Please do not climb fences. There is usually one crater which is unfenced and which may be visited. The features are similar to those seen at Skutustadir (see above), but there are some examples of 'breadcrust bombs' here also. These are tephra fragments which were formed from large (0.3 to 1.0 m diameter) lumps of partially cooled viscous lava, rich in gas, which were ejected from the crater. Their outer surfaces cooled rapidly in contact with the air, giving a glassy skin, while their interiors retained heat. As dissolved gases from the interior came out of solution on cooling, they expanded, giving a vesicular internal structure which had a greater volume than the original lava, thus cracking the skin. The phenomena here, and possibly those at Skutustadir also, may be cinder/spatter cones associated with the Laxa lavas of 3800 or 2000 B.P. The circuit of the lake, back to Skutustadir, may then be undertaken.

The KRAFLA group of sites may also be visited while based near Myvatn. Those adjacent to the vehicle parks can be completed in half a day, but a full day is necessary if visiting the obsidian ridge also.

Leave Reykjahlid on Hy.1, travelling eastwards. After passing the diatomite plant it is possible to make out the line of the graben on the left, as it passes obliquely through the NAMAFJALL moberg ridge. Numerous steaming hot springs and well heads of the Bjarnarflag geothermal power station may be seen, mainly south of the road. On the east side of the ridge, a further collection of hot springs and sulphurous fumaroles can be visited at NAMASKARD**, south of the road and on the eastern slopes of the ridge. Sulphur was once mined here. Very high near-surface temperatures have been recorded in this area; 290°C at only 1.8 km depth was noted during drilling of exploration wells for the Krafla power station. Stop in the vehicle park and explore the hot springs area. GREAT CARE SHOULD BE TAKEN; KEEP TO THE MARKED PATHS. Sulphurous crust near some of the boiling mud pools is only a few millimetres thick.

Leaving here, travel c.1.5 km eastwards and turn left (north) on the road to KRAFLA POWER STATION, built in 1975-77. It is not as efficient as was anticipated because of the tectonically disturbed character of the area. In 1986 only 5 of the 12 high temperature steam wells were working, while in 1990 the operation seemed to be shut down completely. Well casings have been seriously deformed and CO_2 and SO_2 gas pulses have corroded the metal, rendering several wells unusable.

Drive past the power station and take the right fork to the vehicle park

Iceland

near the VITI CRATER. This largely explosive vent was formed during the 1724-29 eruptive sequence and is one of a number which have breached the western rim of 9 km diameter Krafla caldera structure. From here, the area around LEIRNJÚKUR, active most recently in 1984, can be viewed across the valley if access to it is forbidden because of further eruptions or threat of the same. If access is possible, drive down to the lower car park, from which a path leads northwestwards across a shallow graben (Tryggvason, 1980). Five thin lava flows may be distinguished on the 1.5 km walk to the bubbling mud pools and the site of the 1984 eruptions.

The walk to HRAFNTINNUHRYGGUR, the rhyolite/obsidian ridge, is a return trip of about 8 km and requires a half day. Leave the vehicles at the Leirnjúkur car park and walk down hill towards the power station. Take a road on the left (east) which, in recent years has been closed to all but power station traffic. It follows the valley for the initial 1.6 km or so then switch-backs on to a plateau passing some of the geothermal steam well heads. Continue eastwards along what is now only a rough track before climbing on to the ridge. Obsidian at outcrop may be difficult to find except at the southern end of the ridge, but there are many fragments littering the surface. The ridge is thought to be a major 'squeeze-up' structure within the Krafla caldera. From the summit of the ridge, the main Krafla peak can be seen to the northwest and the view to the east embraces the eastern rim (not well defined) of the caldera structure. The obsidian is a rapidly cooled rhyolite which was probably extruded under ice. It is very hard and brittle and should not be hammered. Its sharp edges should also be handled with care. Return along the same track.

ITINERARY 6

The Jökulsá á Fjöllum valley

The features of this valley may be visited as a long day trip from Myvatn or a study of the more important localities could be undertaken en route for the camp site at Hlodaklettar. There is also a range of accommodation at Husavik and further west. The full round trip, outlined here, is best done with a high clearance vehicle. Leaving Reykjahlid on Hy.1, first travel east, crossing the Jökulsá at the Grimsstadir bridge, then turning left (north) on to Hy.864.

28 km from Grimsstadir, the vehicle park for DETTIFOSS is signposted on the west (left) of the road. This fall, the most powerful in Europe, is 44 m high and has a mean flow of 220 m^3 per second, rising to 1500 m^3 in periods of maximum snow melt. In immediate post-glacial times, it is likely that the flow assumed Amazon-like proportions of 0.5 *million* m^3 per second. The 30 km-long gorge of the Jökulsá, plus the abandoned dry

Michael Bamlett and John F. Potter

gorges in the lower course, remain as evidence of the tremendous erosive power and the volume of water involved.

It is possible to walk along the east bank of the river from the car park to another, about 1.1 km northwards, at the SVEINAR cinder cone above the next fall, HAFRAGILSFOSS (27 m), to which the vehicles have transferred.

Views from the path include the columnar jointing of the Pleistocene lavas; the line of the upper tillite (see Figure 21) and the overlying post-glacial lavas at the top of the gorge on the opposite side of the river. Just north of Hafragilsfoss, a post-glacial fissure crosses the gorge at about 45°. The feeder dyke for the Sveinar cone, with horizontal columns and chisel marks, may be examined on the side of the gorge by the more agile members of the party. Another cinder cone, on the opposite side of the gorge also has a feeder dyke but this is not so clear.

Fissures are also visible in the wall of the lower gorge, running north-northeast to south-southwest, parallel to the regional structural trend. These are a continuation of the tensional and volcanic features noted around the Krafla area and near Reykjahlid as part of Itinerary 5.

25 km further north along Hy.864, turn left (west) on to Hy.85. A dry gorge on the left (south) is probably one of the abandoned distributaries of the immediate post-glacial Jokulsá. The river now occupies the most easterly of the three gorges. The third, most westerly gorge is named ASBYRGI and its head, once the site of a major waterfall, may be reached by taking the un-numbered road, the first on the left (south) after the fuel station about 3 km west of the 864/85 junction. After calling at the Visitor Centre (3.5 km down this road) leave vehicles in the parking area at the end of the road.

There are two locations to visit here; firstly the site of the former waterfall, now usually a trickle. The cliffs show thin, post-glacial, mostly olivine tholeiite lavas from STORA VITI (THEISTAREYKJABUNGA) shield volcano, some 20 km to the southwest. The second is the viewpoint on the west side of the gorge, from which the Y-shaped plan of the valley is visible. There are also interesting examples of bottom structures among the lavas, with the overlying flow bases being moulded into the shapes of the ropy surfaces of the underlying pahoehoe. Tephra studies show that some of the Jokulsá water flowed through this part of the valley until at least 2500 B.P.

Leave the gorge by the same route and return to Hy.85, then drive west for a further 1.0 km before turning southwards on Hy.862 to HLODAKLETTAR (Echo Cliffs). After 13 km, take the side track towards the valley. There is a camp site here. Vehicles should be left in the parking area and visitors should take the path towards the river.

About 8000 B.P., a volcanic fissure opened along a south-southeast to north-northwest trend across the Jokulsá which, at that time, would be carrying a huge volume of meltwater from the diminishing ice caps in the south of Iceland. Erupting lava reacted with the river water and a form of Surtseyan activity ensued. The resulting blanket of tephra prevented easy eruption of lava, resulting in an irregular cooling surface on the lava, giving columns at all angles, as the lava pushed up into the unconsolidated tephra. Much of the tephra cover has now been eroded away, revealing the columnar structures. A feeder dyke can be inspected in the valley side at low water, but great care should be taken while close to the river, as water levels can change very abruptly.

Return to vehicles and drive up to the south end of Hy.862. If proceeding to Husavik or further west, return to Hy.85 (see Itinerary 8).

If returning to the Myvatn area, turn left (south) on to what is labelled "jeep track only". Only 4-wheel drive vehicles should use this except in very dry conditions. The track runs between the river and the early Pleistocene shield volcano of GRJOTHÁLS. After 23 km a side track leads eastwards and sub-divides into routes to Hafragilsfoss (northerly) and Dettifoss (southerly). Coaches cannot reach the jeep turning circle at the former, so visitors are faced with a 20-minute (each way) walk to the location above the gorge near Hafragilsfoss. This is a rough walk over sharp, vesicular post-glacial basalts. GREAT CARE SHOULD BE TAKEN WHILE CLOSE TO THE PRECIPITOUS EDGE OF THE GORGE. Below are the fissures mentioned earlier in the context of the Sveinar cone area on the east bank. This feature and its feeder dyke are now visible across the valley.

Return to vehicles and drive to the Dettifoss overlook. Here, the turning circle is accessible for larger vehicles but from here visitors should follow the yellow-painted wooden markers across the top surface of the basalt columns to the flood channel of the Jokulsá and the grassy top level of the gorge. The upper tillite (see Figure 21) is clearly visible, with a red bole above it, succeeded by the post-glacial lava. The columns exhibit chisel marks but poor plumose structures. Return to the jeep track, which becomes even rougher from here on, for the 20 km journey south to Hy.1 and return to Myvatn.

Michael Bamlett and John F. Potter

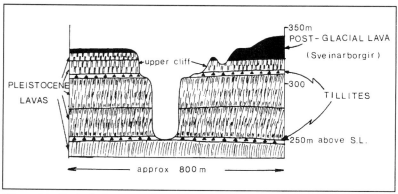

Figure 21: Geological cross section of the Jökulsá gorge north of Dettifoss.

ITINERARY 7

Askja

This journey may be accomplished with a suitable vehicle, either as a day trip from Myvatn or from Egilssatdir, or in transit between the two, with an overnight stop at one of the mountain huts at DREKAGIL or HERDUBREIDARLINDIR, or the camp site at the latter.

From Myvatn

Take Hy.1 eastwards to the turn at Hrossaborg, then the F88 track over the Kollóttodynga lavas, past the tuya of HERDUBREID (1682 m, the highest of this type of volcano in Iceland) to the Drekagil hut. The route then crosses the 1961 lavas, which make driving very difficult in spite of the wooden markers which help to indicate the route, to the gap in the wall of the caldera.

This is about 140 km from Reykjahlid, a good half of which is over very difficult track on post-glacial lavas.

From Egilssatdir

Follow Hy.1 for 72 km to south of Modrudalur (Itinerary 4) then turn south on the F98 track. This route may not be shown on maps published before 1988. Cross the KREPPÁ river, a tributary of the Jokulsá á Fjöllum, after 40 km. (Note – there are good columnar basalts on the slopes of UPPTYPPINGAR, southwest of the bridge). From the Kreppá bridge, it is a further 12 km to a westward turn on to an un-numbered track and 4 km further to the main Jokulsá bridge. From here, there is only one road north

Iceland

to Drekagil and it is 32 km from the Jokulsá bridge to the gap in the caldera wall mentioned above. Only the final 15 km are really difficult driving. The total one-way journey is 160 km.

For the remainder of a short visit, allow a minimum of 4 hours return time from the Drekagil hut.

Passing through the caldera margin, the first site of interest is the collection of five cinder cones which marks the remnants of the 1961 eruption. After examining these, a walk of about 3 km over the airfall deposits of various eruptions between 1875 and 1961 brings the visitor to the VITI CRATER and the overlook of the caldera lake of ÖSKJUVATN.

Askja is only the central part of the 20 km diameter DYNGJUFJÖLL collapse caldera, which is a complex structure- a series of collapses having taken place within what must have been a major sub-glacial structure. Askja is the second (in age) and largest of these collapse features. The third, Öskjuvatn, developed during the 1875 activity.

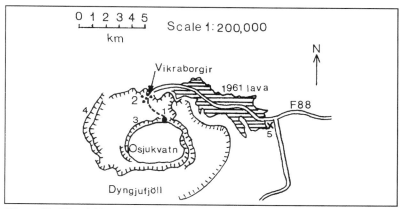

Figure 22: The Askja area.

KEY:
1. Viti crater (formed 1724, active 1875).
2. Cinder cones at head of 1961 lava flow.
3. Margin of Knebel (1875) caldera.
4. Margin of Askja caldera (Pleistocene).
5. Drekagil hut.
- - - - - Approximate route of walk.

Unless the visitor is booked to stay at the Drekagil hut, further exploration of the area is not recommended. However, Figure 22 is included so that those with more time available can examine the area in more detail.

Michael Bamlett and John F. Potter

ITINERARY 8

Asbyrgi to Akureyri

This section may be included as a continuation from the first part of Itinerary 6 (as far as Asbyrgi) or it could begin from the campsite at Hlodaklettar.

Take Hy.85 westwards from the north end of the Asbyrgi track and pass over the northern ends of several tholeiitic lavas from Theistarekyabunga, on which are deserted cliffs and raised beaches similar to those described in Itinerary 1. Around GARDUR, there are screes of wind-blown ash at the base of the abandoned cliff line. This is the northern end of the active zone and these lavas have filled and covered earlier fissures. The active zone continues out into the Arctic Ocean as the AXARFJÖRDUR (or Oxarfjördur) trough, becoming the Kolbeinsey ridge and eventually the Jan Mayen ridge, the alignments of which are dextrally offset by a northwest to southeast transform fault in Axarfjördur bay as part of the TJÖRNES FRACTURE ZONE (Saemundsson, 1974, 1979; Bjornsson *et al* 1979).

At LÓN, a staircase of north-northwest to south-southeast fault line scarps mark the western margin of the Axarfjördur trough and the active zone. The road climbs these and at the summit (HRINGSJA) is a viewpoint on the cliff top, from which the pattern of the distributaries of the Jokulsá á Fjöllum delta and the associated longshore bars may be noted, as well as the extent of the active zone and the northern tuyas of (from north to south) Núpar, Sandfell and Hafrafell.

The road now follows the cliff top around the edge of the TJÖRNES peninsula, which is founded on late Tertiary basalts with tills above. About 20 km beyond Lón, a series of coastal sections in the late Pleistocene glacial sequence exhibit a complex pattern of glacial advance and retreat. Th. Einarsson *et al.* (1967) have identified 10 till layers, some of which are local to this region. The section on the cliff on the west side of BREIDAVIK bay may be examined (ideally through binoculars) from the road. It features the unconformity noted in Table 2 which follows.

TABLE 2

SEQUENCE	TYPICAL ROCKS	SEEN AT
Later lavas	Normal magnetised basalts with tillites.	—
Valadalstorfa lavas	Reverse magnetised basalts	Valadalstorfa
Breidavik Beds	Tillites, thin lavas and cold water marine sediments	Breidavik

UNCONFORMITY

Furuvik Beds	Tillites, normal and reverse magnetised basalts	Furuvik
Tjornes Beds *Cardium* beds *Mactra* beds *Tapes* beds (Late Pliocene)	Mainly littoral and marine fossiliferous sediments showing evidence of climatic cooling up the sequence	Barmur, Hallbjarnarstad-kambur
Late Tertiary	Plateau basalts	Husavik

Some of the detail of the Tjörnes Beds may be examined in a section exposed alongside a track leading down to the small harbour south of HALLBJARNARSTADIR on the west side of the peninsula. A short track leaves Hy.85 on the seaward side. Although some coaches descend to the harbour, it is recommended that transport remains at the top of the hill and visitors walk down the track, examining the highly fossiliferous section shown in Figure 23 as they descend. The assemblage includes gastropods *(Hinia (Nassa) reticulosa)* and the bivalves *Arctica islandica, Cardium greonlandicum, Corbulomya complanata, Macroma* sp., *Spisula (Mactra)* sp. and *Tellina* sp. (Figure 23).

Further descriptions, with a more complete species list may be found in Bardarson (1925), Norton (1977) and Th. Einarsson (1963).

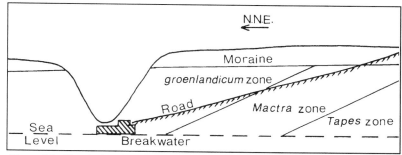

Figure 23: Sketch showing the fossil zones in the cliff section at Hallbjarnarstadir.

The fossils indicate an intertidal/subtidal environment at a time of general climatic cooling, as the first Pleistocene glacial advance occurred about 2 million years ago. All but *Cardium* are tolerant of a wide range of salinities and temperatures. The well-rounded gravel clasts indicate that the lithic material was carried into this site by glacial streams. The cross-bedded layers indicate high energy flow, but contain no fossils.

Continue southwards along Hy.85 to the northern outskirts of HÚSAVIK. Stop briefly alongside the hospital on the left (east) and note that transcurrent faults of the Tjörnes Fracture Zone run approximately east-west through the hospital site. There is accommodation of various types in Húsavik. The bay on which the town stands is called Skjalfandi, which means 'the shaking zone', referring to the frequent occurence of earthquakes along the faults of the Tjörnes Fracture Zone.

If it is required to return to Myvatn, turn on to Hy.87 at LAXIMYRI. En-route note (a) the green houses at Hveravellir and along the Reykjahverfi valley, heated by geothermal water, (b) the small erosion gullies developed on the left (east) of the road in the vicinity of Langavatn. These mark old and now inactive fissures of the Tjörnes Fracture Zone and (c) the large terminal moraine through which the road cuts and south east of which is the outwash sand and gravel plain called Holasandur.

If continuing to Akureyri, continue on Hy.85, crossing the Myrarkvisl and Laxá rivers, then the lavas of the Adaldalshraun, which flowed down much of the Laxá valley in *c.* 2500 B.P., having originated from Krafla. Continue across the north end of the spur of the Tertiary Hafralaekjarbunga and cross another meltwater river from Vatnajökull, the SKJALFANDAFLJÓT, before reaching the junction with Hy.1.

Unless it is included in another itinerary, it is suggested that a visit to the GODAFOSS fall, 4 km to the east, is included here. The fall has a recession gorge* in the post-glacial (*c.*5000 B.P.) Trolladynga lavas, which dominate the east side of the Skjalfandafljót valley. On the east bank note, in the face sectioned by the river between the main fall and the bridges, a number of structures some 4-5 m in diameter, which may have been conduits for steam breaking upwards through the lava to form hornitos on the surface. If these ever existed, they have now been eroded away.

Return to Hy.1 and continue westwards through the LJÓSVATN valley. Adjacent to the road in some drainage ditches layers of pale siliceous ash from Hekla and other volcanic centres may be observed (see Itineraries 1 and 4). No longer is the scenery affected by post-glacial volcanic activity. The Tertiary lavas have been strongly glaciated and there are examples of the associated landforms. The valleys here were ice filled and subsequent

Iceland

melting left the sides well weathered and unsupported, so that rock falls and landslips are common. Near HALS, the road enters a former lake basin which now drains westwards into Eyjafjördur. On its slopes, two terraces may be identified, at 217 m and 88 m above O.D., which mark the water levels (a) before the initial overflow, to the north, along Flateyjardalsheidi and (b) prior to the present overflow into Eyjarfjördur. If time allows, take the longer route along Hys.835 and 83, which demonstrates these features to good advantage. On the right (east) of Hy.835, about 9 km from Hals, is a pit which shows major deformation in the tills. The river which occupies the current outlet valley, the Fnjoská, is one of the few Icelandic rivers which has developed mature meanders in its lower course.

Approaching the bridge over the EYJAFJÖRDUR note, on the left (east), the late Tertiary subaerial basalts dipping at *c.* 20° to the south-southeast which are overlain unconformably by an almost horizontal set of flows which are *c.*5 million years old. In clear weather, the rhyolitic central volcano of Sulur (1144 m) may be seen to the southwest.

Cross the bridge and enter the major town of AKUREYRI, the older part of which is built on a kame, created by meltwater from Glerardalur to the southwest. The delta of the Eyjafjardará has advanced some 2.5 km since the first settlement here.

ITINERARY 9

Akureyri to Drangsnes

This is a long drive (almost 400 km) and will only be undertaken by those wishing to visit the northwest. However, much of the route is on Hy.1 and the interesting sites are well distributed throughout the day. It is possible to sub-divide this itinerary by stopping overnight at Varmahlid, Laugarbakki or Stadur on Hrutafjördur.

Leaving Akureyri and travelling northwards on Hy.1, a group of roches moutonées may be inspected adjacent to the petrol station on the right (east) of the road 2 km from the town centre. Striae indicate ice movement towards the north-northeast. 8 km further on, the road swings into the Horgá valley and then into OXNADALUR. Tertiary lavas, often faulted and with dykes, have been weathered into spectacular pinnacles on the ridge crests. There are also many landslips and a few drumlin fields.

Near the watershed between Oxnadalur and NORDURARDALUR, the side valley of Seldalsfjall is an example of a trough end valley, which was ice filled but lacks a cirque at its head. The effects of soil creep (solifluxion) are evident on many valley sides.

Michael Bamlett and John F. Potter

The NORDURÁ river is joined by several tributaries from the north. The canyons of the VALAGILSÁ and KOTÁ, especially the latter, contain fragments of zeolite-filled vesicular lavas carried down from the plateau. Green celadonite, phacolite (twinned form of chabazite), phillipsite and ordinary chabazite have been collected here.

The road continues into the HERADSVOTN valley, where the bridge is at the head of the deltaic/distributary section. The river here flows on the sediment infill of a glacially-deepened gorge. After VARMAHLID, the road crosses a col, which may be a spillway connecting two pro-glacial lakes, between HELLUFELL (908 m) and KALDBAKUR (965 m), before descending into BLONDUDALUR.

In the valley-side outcrops, the Tertiary lavas now exhibit a lower westward dip angle (10°-15°) as the active zone is left behind. Blondudalur is the access road for the crossing of the centre of Iceland via Hveravellir (Itinerary 13) on the F 37 track. Hy.1 continues to BLONDUOS (Blondosbaer) then southwestwards into VIDIDALUR. The river Vididalsá shows examples of meander development with cut-offs, and there are drumlins on the southwest bank here also. At LAUGARBAKKI there is a geothermal water source and the mountain area to the north is the 7-8 million year old VATNSNESFJALL central volcano.

HRUTAFJÖDUR is too wide to bridge, so the road follows the shore. Hy.1 continues to the south and the itinerary continues on Hy.68. About 2 km north of the junction an example of an esker may be seen on the left (west). Passing through BORDEYRI, reputedly the smallest village in Iceland, drive on to the south shore of BITRUFJÖRDUR, where a roadside outcrop of 6-7 million year old basalts yields zeolites, including heulandite. The rock is flow-sheared.

Almost 6 km further on at OSPAKSEYRI, on the north side of the inlet, there are ice-smoothed and striated rock surfaces. After rounding KOLLAFJORDUR, the road runs slightly inland from the coast on a raised beach. About 8 km after leaving the shore a roadside exposure on the left (south) at HUSAVIKURKLEIF, before Hy.605 is reached, shows a sequence of Tertiary sediments as described in Table 3 below, in an 18 metre long section.

Iceland

TABLE 3 - SECTION AT HUSAVIKURKLEIF

Basalt in 3 flow units ....*c*.3 m total
Mudstone and sands with lobes (load casts) of lava penetrating
downwards and thin penetrations (apophyses) of mud
and sand upwards into the basalt ....0.08 m
A tree bole near the centre of the section and other tree
remains to the north.
Mainly undisturbed mudstones...0.5 m
Interbedded mudstones, sands and lignites, with thick
lignite at base ....0.7 m
Mainly undisturbed mudstone with thick lignite.....................1.9 m
Mainly undisturbed lignite with thin seatearth mudstones
and sands below...1.8 m

Most of the section is cut by a basic dyke, which is 0.6 m wide at its base and which is probably the feeder for the top layer of the basalt. It seems that the section is fault-bounded on the west. The uppermost sediments are baked by the lowest lava and also by the dyke. The heat from the dyke has altered the lignites in its vicinity to coke and some of the lignites have been coalified by heat from the dyke and the lavas. Fossil insects have been found here in the mudstones.

Proceed around STEINGRIMSFJÖRDUR to the bridge over the river at its head, near STAKKANES, then follow Hy.645 along the northern shore of the fjörd, passing the ruins of a former geothermally heated swimming pool at HVERAVIK. At the village of DRANGSNES sleeping bag accommodation is available in the community hall. There are zeolites and a dyke near the harbour and, if a complete day is spent here, an outcrop similar to that seen at Husavikurkleif can be visited on the southeastern slope of BAEJARFELL. There are also lignites, which outcrop just below the 200 m contour, paleosols and weathered lava surfaces on the slope above the harbour.

ITINERARY 10

Drangsnes to Snaefellsnes

Only the extremely dedicated, or those with time to spare will venture further north-west, maybe to see the Drangjökull icecap or to examine the small rhyolite outcrops at Reykjarfjördur, Bláfell in Skoraheidi and Tjaldanesfell (where there is also a gabbro). There is also a wealth of glacial features, but nothing which cannot be seen elsewhere.

Michael Bamlett and John F. Potter

This itinerary, however, now turns southwards along the western side of the broad isthmus which links the northwestern fjörds to the main part of the country. Leave Drangsnes by Hy.645, then join Hy.61, which runs along Steingrimsfjardarheidi (the STADARDALUR pass) through high, intensely glaciated upland.

Turn left (south) on to Hy.608 and, after about 14 km, stop at a suitable viewpoint overlooking THORSKAFJÖRDUR. At this location look for stone stripes or polygons and other evidence of periglacial action. Note the numerous lakes on the ice scoured plateau; the unusual calc-alkaline volcano to the east of KROJKSFJÖRDUR to the south-southeast and the twin rhyolite domes of KAMBSFJALL.

The road (now Hy.60) continues through this area, past the tidal dominated delta at the head of Thorskafjördur, then around GILSFJÖDUR into the pass of HVOLSDALUR-SVEINADALUR. In climbing the latter, note the numerous dykes in both walls of the valley. On the descent there are numerous waterfalls. Continue on Hy.60 to Hy.57, then turn right (west) into the SNAEFELLSNES PENINSULA. Accommodation is available in several places, including STYKKISHOLMUR, (Stykkisholmsbaer), ÓLAFSVIK, (north coast), ARNARSTAPI and LÝUSHÓLL (south coast).

ITINERARY 11

The Snaefellsnes Peninsula

Ideally, this takes at least 2 days. It is set out here as a continuous sequence, so that visitors may reject sections which do not appeal to them or for which time is not available. Starting in the northeastern corner, where Hy.57 branches from Hy.60, travel west for about 50 km along the southern shore of HVAMMSFJÖRDUR, across Tertiary basalts. As the road rounds the inlet of ALTARFJÖRDUR look back from the southwest to the northeastern side to see large landslips and dykes near the cliff top. The inland continuation of the valley is another example of a trough-end.

The rhyolite dome of DRAPUHLIDARFJALL may be approached on foot from the north side, to examine some of the rocks exposed by the major landslip there. Devitrified obsidian and banded rhyolite may be found.

Take the right (north) turn and drive to STYKKISHÓLMUR from where boat trips are normally available to Flatey and return (about 4 hours) or a 2-hour trip 'round the bay' to see the (?) unique columnar basalts which make up the skerries at the entrance to Hvammsfjördur. This is a better option for geologists. Fuel and food supplies are also available in the town.

Although sheet 2 of the 1:250,000 geological map shows Holocene fossils in alluvium just to the west of the junction of Hys.56 and 57 at SKJÖLDUR, the thin, braided deposit of fine sand has failed to yield any to recent visitors. However, a rhyolite flow from DRAPUHLIDAR may be inspected at the base of the section, capped by a paleosol or weathered surface, and a 2 m thick olivine-plagioclase basalt, with crude columns at its base and a rubbly top with elongate vesicles.

Take Hy.57 westwards towards Ólafsvik. West of the junction with Hy.56, note the row of Strombolian explosion craters south of the road and the BESERKJAHRAUN, which is the post-glacial lava and air-fall deposit associated with the most westerly of the row. The road continues round to GJAFI promontory, which is composed of gabbro in the north and rhyolite in the south. Collectors may take the opportunity to sample from the talus alongside the road, on the west side of the hill.

Take Hy.576 around the SETBERG peninsula (Sigurdsson, 1970, much quoted in other publications). Below KLAKUR summit, on the east side, the acid agglomerate may be sampled in the extensive talus. Energetic visitors may climb to the summit to inspect the ankaramite* cap .

Continue around the peninsula and stop at the Setberg burial ground on the east side of the road. On the coast here, examine an acid ignimbrite tuff which overlies a basaltic andesite flow (CARE NEEDED), below the road. Drive on a further 15 km or so to BULANDSHOFDI where two layers of conglomeratic tillite are covered and protected by alkali basalt flows.

In ÓLAFSVIK, there is accommodation and food supplies. Sometimes it is possible to arrange a summer night-time visit to the summit of SNAEFELLSJÖKULL (the ice is too soft during the day). Enquire at the Hotel Nes. This involves coach transport, preferably with your own vehicle, up a rough track to the ice margin, followed by transport to the ice-cap summit by tracked vehicle. MAKE SURE THAT YOUR INSURANCE COVERS THIS. The western end of the Snaefellsnes peninsula is probably the best section to visit if only one day is available.

Travel west from Ólafsvik through Rif and Hellissandur on Hy.574. There are 10 craters on the NESHRAUN lava field, two of them in the area named SAXHOLAR. The road was re-aligned here in 1990, so take extra care with locations. Drive off the road if possible and walk $c.100$m across the aa surface (CARE NEEDED) towards a crater, until a 40 m wide and 4 m deep depression, running approximately south to north on the lava surface is encountered. This is a lava channel which issues from a breach in the eastern wall of the crater and follows a curving course before dividing into a number of subsidiary channels. There is a levée on the inner side of the bend and some 'break-out' structures on the outer side. There are also some small lava tubes or tunnels along the edges of the flow, but the structure never had an overall 'roof'. Various sub-horizontal flow structures may be noted in the walls and various vertical 'scratch' marks may be due to small scale, slide-down faulting while the lava was still plastic.

Return to transport and continue to the signposted drive-in crater of HOLAHOLAR, which comprises low volume lava flows interbedded with pyroclastic falls, which dominate the surface now. A few breadcrust (see Itinerary 5) and 'spindle'* bombs may be found.

On Hy.574 once more, continue the circuit eastwards, noting the prominent sea stacks at LONDRANGAR, which are probably the cores of ancient craters.

Take the un-numbered side road on the south to the village of HELLNAR and, if possible, arrange for the transport to go forward to ARNARSTAPI. Take the cliff-top path towards the northeast, noting the following features, some of which recur (BEWARE of attacks by nesting birds (terns and fulmars) on this walk): 1. A fine-grained, possibly chilled, acid (?dacitic) lava, with small plagioclase phenocrysts, which appears to have flowed and slumped into the predominantly vesicular basaltic lavas while the latter were still plastic, or perhaps due to the partial remelting at the junction between them. The lava was erupted from a flank crater in the main Snaefellsjökull volcano, 2. A flaggy, well-weathered outcrop of this lava (or associated air fall deposit) in the lower part of the cliff, 3. Inter-mixing of the two lava types, probably due to partial, marginal re-melting, 4. A layer of tillite, some 4-5 m thick, with clear, conglomeratic layers, in a small bay, 5. Close to Arnarstapi a fine example of columnar basalt at the base of a small headland, continued into the next bay to the northeast, 6. A natural arch and a hole in the headland and 7. Just south of Arnarstapi fishing harbour, 3 blow holes, developed above caves cut by marine erosion along the joints in the basalts.

Return to transport and, proceeding eastwards, note the BADAHRAUN crater and surrounding lava. Take Hy.54 where Hy.574 joins it at Budir, then turn left (north) along the loop road (Hy.572) to LYUSHÓLL and park at the community centre. Walk up the steep valley to the north (LYSUSKARD). At least three craters lie in the mountains above, and the deformed and faulted mixture of rock types on the eastern wall (in particular) of the valley indicates at least two phases of injection/intrusion by andesitic and acidic magmas into what was probably an original series of basaltic flows. The activity is probably connected to the LJOSUFJÖLL

Iceland

central volcano, some 30 km to the east. It is understood that garnets have been found in rocks in this area. On the slope leading into the valley, look for stone stripes and other periglacial features.

At STADASTADUR, 9 km from the eastern 572/54 junction, just north of the road, the 'father of the Icelandic sagas' ARI FRODI THORGILSSON (Ari the wise), 1068-1148 A.D. is supposed to have lived. A mineral spring provides water which ensures longevity (?) and a memorial states:

> EN HVATKI ER MISSAGT
> ER I FRAEDUM THESSUM
> PA ER SKYLT AD HAFA
> PAD HELDUR ER SANNARA
> REYNIST

(Essentially- 'If my sources are not reliable, I will not quote them'.)

A wisdom we should all respect!

25 km east of the 54/56 junction, a minor, un-numbered road leads northwards along the eastern slopes of RAUDAMELSFJALL, past the farm of Gerduberg and a wall of basaltic lava columns. 5.5 km along this road, park and walk across the field on the left. Cross the stream and head for a dilapidated shed to sample another mineral spring, which is faintly effervescent. Examine the adjacent aa lava front which issues from the eastern flank of the Ljosufjöll volcano for zeolites. There is also a fine waterfall here.

Return to Hy.54 and in 6 km turn left (north) on to Hy.55. 12 km along this, park at a farm called HEGGSTADIR. From here, there is a 2 hour return walk to a major lava cave, GULLBORGARHELLIR, on the western flanks of Gullborg, to the west. Entry permits must be obtained from the farm.

Retrace to Hy.54 and turn left (south) for 6 km, then turn right (west) on to an un-numbered road opposite the airstrip, which reaches a dead-end at a farm called SNORRASTADIR. Coaches with more than 30 seats are advised not to attempt this road. From the farm, a marked footpath leads to ELDBORG crater (112 m). The walk, by an active group, should take about 1 hour each way. This is part of a post-glacial crater row, 2 of which may be seen at Eldborg and another at BARNABORGARHRAUN to the southeast. According to *The Book of Settlements*, Eldborg erupted in about 900 A.D. and two distinct lavas may be identified, the more recent retaining its ropy surface. Those who climb to the crater rim will note the predominance of lavas over pyroclastic deposits, although the lavas which have flowed away from the vent are only a few centimetres thick.

Michael Bamlett and John F. Potter

Return to Hy.54 and continue south towards BORGANES, Hy.1 and the following itinerary (12).

ITINERARY 12

Thingvellir, Geysir and Gullfoss

From Borganes, where there is accomodation and supplies, follow Hy.1 northeastwards (N.B. Do NOT cross the bridge over the Borgarfjördur) for 8 km then turn right on to Hy.52, following the Grimsá river upstream. There is sleeping bag accommodation at BRAUTARTUNGA (and also a farm called "England" which is now deserted).

Continue on Hy.52 until it turns sharply to the south, 23 km from Brautatunga. It is possible for properly equipped vehicles to take the 53 km track (which has several fords) across to Gulfoss, allowing this itinerary to be conducted in reverse sequence. The scheme outlined here uses the more universally passable roads.

Turn south on Hy.52 and in 24 km THINGVELLIR is reached (Figure 24). Here, a vivid example of the summit graben of the Mid-Atlantic Ridge, which is a continuation of the Reykjanes Ridge in the North Atlantic, may be seen on land. The actual ridge is displaced eastwards by four sets of *en echelon* faults in the peninsula between Thingvellir and Keflavik. This is clearly visible on geological maps and also see Aronson & Saemundsson (1975).

The total width of the graben structure between the outermost faults is *c*.5 km and it may be traced longitudinally for about 25 km from the southwestern end of Thingvallavatn to near Lagafell adjacent to Hy.52. The American Plate lies on the northwestern side; the Eurasian one on the southeastern. Further detail is shown on Figure 24.

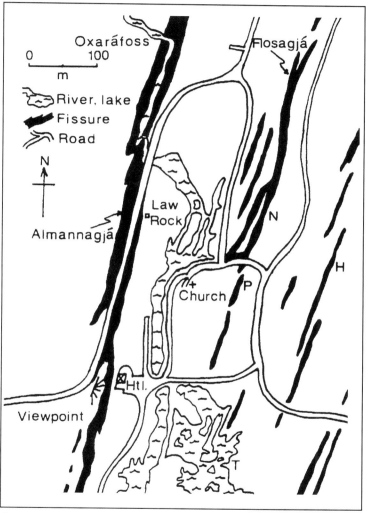

*Figure 24: The Thingvellir area. N - Nikulásargjá, H – Háagjá,
P – Peningagjá, Htl – Hotel, T – Thingvallavatn.*

Michael Bamlett and John F. Potter

Associated with the 40 m high fault scarps on either side of the graben there are a number of minor clefts (gjás), some of which may be visited. The site of the original meetings of *The Althing* (Iceland's parliament) at LOGBERG (the Law Rock), is one such on the northwest side. Hy.36 links the two sides, running across the 9000 year old pahoehoe lavas which come from the classic shield volcano SKALDBREIDUR (1060 m) to the northeast. The graben widened 2 cm during 1970-73 (Decker *et al*, 1976) and, although recent subsidence has been negligible, the floor has dropped an estimated 70 m during historic times. The most recent volcanic activity took place around 2000 years ago, when the twin tephra cones on Sandey island in Thingvallavatn were formed and the southwest corner of the lake was invaded by the NESJAHRAUN lavas.

After visiting Thingvellir leave by Hy.365. After about 5 km from the northeast corner of the lake, park by the roadside and walk 30-40 m on the north side of the road to a hornito mound which is linked to a deep lava tunnel. Observation of the adjacent ground (CARE NEEDED) will reveal a line of roof collapses into this tube.

A further 2 km drive brings visitors to the artificial cave of LAUGARVATNSHELLIR, in the Surtseyan type tephra on the southern slopes of Laugarvatnsfjall. The predominantly fine grained material of the cave layer is overlain by a coarser, brecciated sequence, in which some large fragments of pillow structures may be noted. Exploration of the narrow valley east of the cave reveals a set of pillow lavas (bolstraberg), providing evidence of sub-aqueous (probably sub-glacial) origin of these rocks. The absence of a subaerial lava indicates that this eruptive sequence did not have enough energy to reach the upper surface of the englacial lake and thus failed to form a tuya (for explanation, see Introduction).

At LAUGARVATN, turn left (northeast) and follow Hy.57 then Hy.35 to GEYSIR. The Great Geysir rarely spouts now, but STROKKUR provides a fountain every 10-15 minutes (erratic), reaching up to 40 m from the crest of its shallow geyserite (siliceous sinter) dome (for explanation, see Introduction).

Continue for 9 km on Hy.37 to the vehicle park at GULFOSS (31 m), the average discharge of which is 118 m^3/sec., rising to 2000 m^3/sec. in flood conditions. The fall is controlled by 2 sets of faults, north-northeast to south-southwest and northeast to southwest. The main (upper) fall is over a basalt flow, which protects the more easily eroded materials below it (Figure 25).

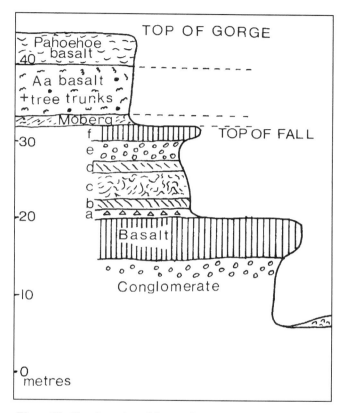

Figure 25: Sketch section of the stratigraphy at Gullfoss.

KEY:

    f. basalt
    e. conglomerate
    d. cross-bedded sandstone
    c. frost-disturbed siltstone
    b. cross-bedded sandstone
    a. tillite

Michael Bamlett and John F. Potter

Explore the western side of the fall and look for frost-disturbed Pleistocene siltstones and cross-bedded sandstones, lithified by heat from the overlying lavas. The recession gorge* is *c.*2.5 km long and must have been eroded during post-glacial time (the last 10,000 years).

Rest-room facilities have recently been built near the upper car and coach park here.

From Gulfoss, retrace to Geysir, then follow Hy.35 for 40 km. On the southeast side of the road is the phraeto-magmatic explosion crater of KAERLID, on the slopes of Grimsnes. Rising magma invaded an area saturated with ground water and the resulting interaction produced this feature.

From here, continue to Selfoss and rejoin Hy.1, turning west into REYKJAVIK after about 48 km. An alternative to a night in the capital could be at BRAUTARHOLT, 28 km to the northeast via Hys.1 and 30.

ITINERARY 13

Akureyri, Hveravellir and Reykjavik

Itineraries 1 to 12 cover a roughly circular trip around Iceland. Numbers 13 and 14 deal with two routes across the central desert plateau. Both link to other itineraries at either end.

From Akureyri in the north of the island, follow Itinerary 9 as far as BLONDUDLAUR, where the road up the valley (south), near the hydro-electric station, should be taken (Hys.731/732). There is a fuel station at EYVINDARSTADIR, but it is recommended that sufficient fuel for 300 km should be carried from VARMAHLID, or an adjacent fuel point.

Travelling south, views of the ice caps HOFSJÖKULL, HRUTFELL and LANGJÖKULL may be had from the upland sandur. Much of this valley may be flooded in due course by the development of hydro-electric projects involving the Blandá river and the road may be re-aligned. Visitors are recommended to check that they are on the F37 track by use of the most recent map and a compass.

After 72 km from Eyvindarstadir, take the side track on the right (west) to HVERAVELLIR where campsite and mountain hut accommodation are available. The accommodation site is located at the head of a shallow valley with geothermally heated springs. It lies just north of the main Icelandic watershed and at the eastern margin of the western active zone.

When natural hot water reaches the surface, mini-terraces of geyserite

Iceland

(siliceous sinter, $SiO_2.nH_2O$) form as the silica comes out of solution as the water cools. These terraces, which are only a few millimetres high at each step, are only formed when the emission of the water is non-explosive (geyser-type effusions usually tend to build bee-hive shaped structures) (Francis, 1976, p.296). Collinson & Thompson (1981) draw attention to the role of heat-loving algae in the removal of silica from solution. Each terrace has a low rim of silica created where evaporation at the edge of the terrace pool is greatest.

Leaving Hveravellir, clear weather gives views of the 1000 m high tuya of KLALFELL and the smaller shield volcano of STRYTUR some 5 km to the north. It is important to check the compass regularly here as there are several small, unsigned side tracks which may appear to be the main road. The situation on this score is, however, improving.

28 km from Hveravellir, an un-numbered road to the east, which may be signposted 'Arskard/Arskardsfjell/Ski School', may be taken towards the rhyolitic dome of KERLINGARFJÖLL and the twin, ice-covered rhyolite peaks of SNAEKOLLUR (1477 m) and SVARTHYRNA (1158 m). There are sulphurous fumaroles at the head of the valley. Beside the track on the south, and possibly best visited on the return journey (this is a dead-end valley) is the fall of GYGJARFOSS, with a sectioned exposure of fluvio-glacial sands, etc. adjacent to it. The complete trip along this valley is *c*.20 km and about 2 hours should be allowed for group visits.

Returning to F37 and continuing southwards, the shield volcanoes of BALDHEIDI (771 m) and LEGGABRJOTUR (1026 m) may be noted on the right (west). Half of the latter is submerged beneath the Langjökull ice cap. If the loop to HVITARVATN is taken (there is a mountain hut there) note the ice floes on the lake, detached from the Skridufell section of the Langjökull ice.

The road now climbs southwestwards around the slopes of BLÁFELL tuya (1204 m), the highest peak in southwest Iceland, to a large cairn at the (locally) highest point of the road. Views to the west are dominated by the JARLHETTUR basaltic moberg crater row, at the southeasterly edge of the Langjökull ice. An un-numbered track leaves F37 following the SANDÁ river (a tributary of the Hvitá) towards the southern end of this feature, where there is a mountain hut. South of the ford across the Sandá, and opposite the airstrip, there are further examples of roches moutonées, with striations trending westwards (Kjartansson 1955).

The mountain track ends at GULLFOSS and it is recommended that visitors should follow part of Itinerary 12 in reverse (Gullfoss-Geysir-Thingvellir) and then return to Reykjavik or continue to Borganes for a visit

Michael Bamlett and John F. Potter

to Snaefellsnes (Itinerary 11).

ITINERARY 14

Reykjahlid-Nyidalur-Landmannalaugar-Eldgja-South Coast; The Sprengisandur

This is a testing drive at the best of times. It is STRONGLY RECOMMENDED that it should be split into two day-long sections, with a break being taken at one of the following- Nyidalur, Landmannalaugar, Veidivotn or Versalir.

From Reykjahlid, follow Hy.1 to Godafoss, through LAUGAR where there are hot springs. The turn off southwards (left) after taking on fuel for *c.* 350 km (to Hrifunes on Hy.1 in the south via Landmannalaugar and Eldgjá).

Take the Hy.844 along the BARDARDALUR, which exhibits flood basalts of post-glacial age from TROLLADYNGA on the east, and Tertiary basalts on the west. Cross the bridge at SANDVIK and turn right for about 80-100 m. Here on the left (west) is the farm of STORUVELLIR. Negotiate permission to view the exposures adjacent to the steeply-graded tributary valley behind the farm. In the south wall of this valley is a sequence of basalts and a conglomeratic tillite, with a dyke cutting the lower layers. There are zeolites (mainly chabazite) and chalcedony in some of the vesicular basalts. A soft, brown material in some vesicles is the clay mineral, saponite.

Resume the southward journey on Hy.842, passing MYRI the last farm for 240 km before driving down a short (0.5 km) side track to the fall at ALDEYARFOSS on the Skalfandafljót river. It cascades over a 20 m high set of confused curvilinear columns beneath a rubbly hyaloclastite. Some of the columns are curved (see Introduction).

On the top of the gorge on the far (east) side is a post-glacial lava, which has been responsible for diverting the river, while on the west, visitors may walk on the pot-holed, rocky former river bed.

The F28 mountain track is now followed. After *c.*35 km a set of roches moutonées may be examined on the left (east) of the track, between this and the river. The striae and form indicate a northward ice movement.

Some 6 to 7 km south of the junction with the F78 track (on the right/west), is the main Icelandic watershed. Some 12 km further on, alongside the 'lifeless' lake of FJÖRDUNGSVATN, which occasionally dries up, and near the junction with the F72 track is the legendary 'centre of Iceland'. Alongside the road mostly to the left, (east), are a series of large

Iceland

(c.30 m) diameter polygons, which occur on the relatively flat, stony desert. They form shallow ditches about 0.7 m wide and a maximum 0.3 m deep, with mosses growing in the base. Washburn (1956) and Thorarinsson (1964) have reviewed these features and Rapp & Annerssten (1969) provide a lengthy and speculative possible explanation of their periglacial origin.

A further 15 km or so brings the visitor to NÝIDALUR, where there is a camping ground and two tourist huts. In the valley to the southeast, called Nýidalur or Jökuldalur, there are more large polygons and also some dykes in the northern wall.

From c.20 km south of Nýidalur, the rhyolitic moberg mountains of HYRDRI HÁGANGA (1278 m) and SYDRI HÁGANGA (1284 m) may be noted on the left (east) side of the track.

Approaching the lake of THORISVATN after passing Saudafell on the left (east), the glacial meltwater river KALDAKVISL, which starts from western Vatnajökull, is crossed (on a bridge). Note the double set of columnar basalts. Some of the water from this river has been diverted into Thorisvatn to supplement supplies for the SIGALDA hydro-electric scheme.

Near the south end of the lake, the F28 mountain track ends. If proceeding to VEIDIVOTN take the left (eastern) turn on to an un-numbered track here and continue east and then south for c.25 km. There are tourist huts here among the lakes, which were impounded by post-glacial basaltic flows and pyroclastic material. The regional rifting trend from northeast to southwest is well shown by the alignment of the crater rows and the related pattern of Pleistocene and post-glacial lava flows. The return is by the same route to the south end of Thorisvatn.

Continue for 9 km on Hy.32 then, at the generating dam of the Sigalda hydro-electric power station, take the F22 track south towards FROSTASTADAVATN. Just before reaching the lake, it is worth taking an un-numbered road on the left (east) to visit the lake-filled explosion crater LJÓTIPOLLUR.

The campsite and huts at LANDMANNALAUGAR are reached by way of the small (0.75 km diameter) post-glacial NORDURNAMUR caldera.

The F22 track cuts across the rim of this above Frostastadavatn and it is worth stopping here to gain an overall view of the structure. Early explosive activity built the tephra walls. This was followed by a basaltic lava eruption which filled the crater, before overflowing on the south and spreading eastwards into the TUNGNÁA valley. Finally, the STUTUR cinder cone developed west of the centre of the 'caldera'. There is a path to the rim of

Michael Bamlett and John F. Potter

this cone and pyroclastic tephra 'bombs' may be seen on the slopes. There is also a small lava tube on the west side, adjacent to the road.

From here, it is only 4 km to the upper camp site, reached by turning right (southwest) off the F22 track and continuing 2 km into the northern section of the TORFAJÖKULL volcanic centre. The camp site is surfaced with stones!

If not staying here, it is nevertheless worth leaving the transport near the camp site and walking round between the southeastern margin of the post-glacial LAUGARHRAUN rhyolite flow and the Pleistocene rhyolitic moberg. A block of unusual columnar rhyolite from the latter may be noted, adjacent to the stream and in the cliff beyond. A further 500 m upstream the lava overlies a glacial till.

Exploration of the surface of the flow reveals specimens of red and black banded rhyolite, including some which has been squeezed just prior to solidifying and which appears rather like a large discharge of toothpaste. There are also numerous pitchstone fragments.

The lava source lies on BRENNISTEINALDA close to a group of sulphur fumaroles, where fragile sulphur crystals may be seen. The flow surface is a network of paths and a return to the transport or camp site should make use of these. Warm springs issuing from beneath the 15 m high flow front provide bathing pools.

Rejoin the F22 track and continue southeastwards, leaving the area at KIRKJUFELL (964 m), a rhyolite dome. Drive southeast across late Pleistocene hyaloclastites and tuffs for about 30 km to reach ELDGJÁ fissure. This is reached by turning left (northeast) off the F22. An un-numbered side track penetrates some 2 km into the valley, but the spectacular section to the northeast has to be explored on foot. This southwest to northeast eruption fissure is part of a 40 km long feature which extends from Gjátindur at the northeast end to (and almost certainly beneath) the Mydralsjökull. It lies about 5 km to the north of and parallel to the Laki fissure (see Itinerary 3).

Eldgjá's recent eruptive activity was in 930-934 A.D., when most of the 8.2 km long, 600 m wide and 200 m deep fissure was created. The early activity was subaqueous, and Surtseyan type explosive activity built the layers of pyroclastic debris which form much of the valley slopes. This built up above water level and subaerial fire fountains deposited the lava spatter layer, which caps the hills on either side and dips steeply (35°) towards the valley floor on the upper slopes. At times, the fissure lava overflowed towards the southwest end and ran down the SKAFTÁ valley, spreading out over the coastal lowland to cover about 700 sq.km. Part of this was later

Iceland

covered by the Laki flows of 1783 and by alluvium deposited by the Skaftá. For a map of the lavas, see Figure 14.

At a late stage, as the lava level declined, small spatter cones developed on the fissure floor. The walk along the valley passes these and eventually reaches the OFAERUFOSS waterfall. Its natural bridge, which collapsed during June 1993, was a feature formed by the differential erosion between the softer, underlying pyroclastic material and the harder overlying lavas. The climb up to the bridge site is strenuous. GREAT CARE IS ESSENTIAL IF VENTURING CLOSE TO THE FALLS.

The visit here, from leaving the transport, climbing to the bridge site and return, will occupy 2.5 to 3 hours. Return now to the F22 track and travel south across Laki lavas of 1783 and late Pleistocene moberg west of the Skaftá valley, to BÚLAND, where the mountain track ends and Hy.208 links to Hy.1 south of Uthlid. This links to Itineraries 2 and 3.

ITINERARY 15A

The Westmann Islands (Vestmannaeyjar) (by J.F. Potter and R. Toynton)

The main island of HEIMAEY may be reached by air from Reykjavik (not Keflavik) airport or by sea from THORLAKSHOFN, 38 km southeast of the capital, via Hys. 1, 39 and 38. While the air trip can give a one-day 'snapshot' of the island, an overnight stay allows time to look at the geology on land and for a short boat trip to view coastal features.

The oldest rocks in the islands are no more than 10,000 years old (post-glacial), but the main geological attraction is the phenomena associated with the 1973 eruption which created the new volcano ELDFELL, and the lava which flowed north from it to the harbour mouth (Figure 26).

The oldest part of the island is the range of moberg hills (Dalsfjall) which form the northern flank. The western extremity of this contains the crater of HERJOLFSDALUR, normally a camp site, but also forming the arena for the National Festival in August. On the seaward side of this, columnar basalt forms the cliffs.

Michael Bamlett and John F. Potter

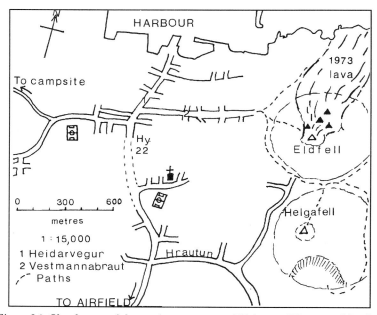

Figure 26: Sketch map of the northeastern area of Heimaey, Westmann Islands.

The 1973 activity started along a fissure line northeast of the old volcano of HELGAFELL, with about 20 cinder cones developing along a 2 km section aligned approximately north-south. After 24 hours, the eruption had centralised at what became Eldfell and a month of Strombolian activity built a 200 m high scoria cone. A thick mantle of ash and pyroclastic debris covered the town, causing many fires (Self *et al*, 1974).

The crater filled with lava, which eventually broke a section out of the northern rim and carried it on the flow surface towards the eastern end of the harbour. The progress of the flow was halted, partly by pumping about 6 million tonnes of sea water on to the lava. A 40 m high cliff of clinkery lava and columnar basalt now marks the lava front, some of which has already been eroded away by the sea.

To view the two volcanic peaks, the following routes are recommended:

(i) From the harbour walk southwest along HEIDARVEGUR and turn left (east) at VESTMANNABRAUT. Follow this to the end where the margin of the 1973 lava is reached. Turn right and head for the col between the two peaks.

(ii) To attain the same point from the airport, walk north on Hy.22 and turn right (east) at the first crossroads, on to HRAUNTUN. Follow this road round the southeast margin of the town, taking the second turning on the left, along the western base of Helgafell, until the col road is reached on the right (east). Each of these routes is about 1.5 km long. Then, from the col summit, it is possible to ascend (scramble) to the summit of Helgafell, from which there are impressive views.

The summit crater of Helgafell is a small, sub-circular scoria-lined depression. (On the south side there is an abandoned quarry, now used as a domestic waste tip).

Return to the col road, turn right and around the base of Helgafell into the quarry. The section (if still visible) is mostly bedded pyroclastics. In the centre of the face is a lava-filled channel which has been cut into the pyroclastic surface.

Retrace now to the vicinity of the 1973 lava, the KIRKJUBAEJAHRAUN, and examine the cinder cone row and look for spindle pyroclastic bombs among the grass on the adjacent hillside. It is possible to walk on to the aa-type flow but GREAT CARE IS NEEDED. It is strongly recommended that thick gardening or builders' gloves are worn and that the potential for serious injury is realised if visitors fall on the jagged, sharp-edged lava fragments. The lava can also tear the toughest boots.

There is a well-marked path to a lava tunnel, some 30 m on to the flow. It is about 4 m wide and 4-5 m high. In 1990 it was possible to walk through, but this will change as the flow settles down and weathering affects its stability. The walls of the tunnel are covered with pull-apart structures, similar to those on the Dimmuborgir pillars, but much fresher (see Itinerary 5).

Down-flow from the tunnel, there is a section of smoother pahoehoe ropy lava, which is easy to walk on, but it must be remembered that this is the thin roof of the continuation of the tunnel! This is part of the highly fluid lava which was erupted towards the end of the sequence in May-June 1973. (Tr. Einarsson, 1974).

There is a path around the base of Eldfell, with good views of the lava's aa surface. In many places it has broken into slabs which, at their inception, were riding on an unevenly flowing molten mass below.

Heimaey now obtains much of its hot water by using the residual heat in this lava, so the ground is usually warm all around this vicinity. A path leads to the crater rim of Eldfell, where there are sulphurous fumaroles.

Michael Bamlett and John F. Potter

Alternatively, the breach in the crater rim, where the lava break-out occurred, may be visited. Return to the town, harbour or airport as appropriate.

ITINERARY 15B

Reykjavik

If a day or part of a day is to be spent in Reykjavik (Figure 27), there are three geologically-interesting places which may be visited:

(i) The Natural History Museum, in HLEMMUR near the city 'bus station. Although it is only two rooms, the display of zeolites and other Icelandic materials and rocks makes it worth a visit. Open 4 days per week, in afternoons only, so please check first. It may be possible to arrange special opening for parties at other times – Telephone (in 1991) 91-25540.

KEY:

1.	Air terminal	11.	Hallgrimskirkja (church)
2.	University of Iceland	12.	New Youth Hostel (+ swimming baths)
3.	Saga Hotel		
4.	Pond	13.	Old Youth Hostel
5.	Reykjavik City Hall	14.	Ellidavogur cliff section(opposite marina)
6.	Nordic House		
7.	Öskjuhlid hot water tanks	15.	Major road interchange
8.	Hotel Loftleidir (and coach to Keflavik airport)	16.	Hofdi house
		17.	Natural History Museum (and Bus Station)
9.	BSi coach terminal		
10.	Central Shopping Area	18.	City Hospital

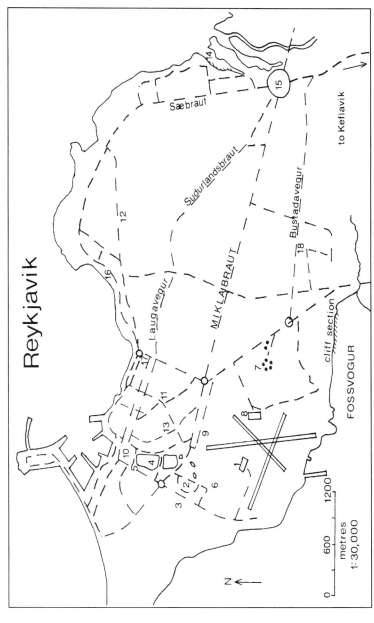

Figure 27: Reykjavik location map. (Key opposite)

Michael Bamlett and John F. Potter

(ii) The storage tanks for the city's hot water (and the cylindrical restaurant) stand on a low hill at ÖSKJUHLID, west of the Skogarhlid road and east of Reykjavik airport. Walking southeast from here, fossiliferous late Pleistocene and Holocene sediments may be i investigated. About 5 m thickness of marine siltstones are poorly exposed in excavations, yielding small gastropods and various bivalves, including *Astarte* and *Mactra*. The underlying cliff section on the northern banks of the FOSSVOGUR give a better outcrop as follows:

TABLE 5 (a) – Cliff section on south coast at Fossvogur, Reykjavik

Buff-yellow sandstone with included basalt
boulders up to 0.2 m diameter towards base ....c.2.0 m

Cross-bedded glacial outwash sands with
basalt pebbles ....c.1.0 m

Tillite with basalt boulders up to 1.0 m diameter.......1.15 m

Buff-yellow sandstone with included basalt boulders
up to 0.2 m diameter towards base ....c.2.0 m

Cross-bedded glacial outwash sands with
basalt pebbles ....c.1.0 m

Tillite with basalt boulders up to 1.0 m diameter ......1.15 m

Irregular base

Buff-yellow sandstone with bivalves in life positions
and occasional basalt boulders up to 0.2 m diameter
(mixed debris from melt of floating ice?) ....up to 2.0 m

Irregular base with cobbles up to 0.15 m diameter

Cryoturbated, finely laminated siltstone.....................seen for 0 to 0.5 m

Grey basalts ....poorly shown

Iceland

(iii) It is recommended that wheeled transport is hired to reach the site of inter-glacial deposits, including a thin lignite, at ELLIDAVOGUR on the shore of the Ellidaá river on the east side of the Reykjavik peninsula. Take the dual carriageway, MIKLABRAUT to the east-southeast, taking the exit to the north at the big interchange before the Ellidá river is crossed. Travel about 300 m along Ellidavogur and turn right on to Sudavogur. It is suggested that a parking place is found here and the shoreline explored on foot. The sequence visible (location varies with the state of the shore) is as follows:

TABLE 5 (b) – Sequence on the Ellidavogur shore, Reykjavik

Lignite	0.2 m
Till/conglomerate (northern part)	variable
Buff-yellow cross-bedded sands	2-3 m
Fine brown clay with shell-rich lenses	4-5 m

72

Michael Bamlett and John F. Potter

REFERENCES

ARONSON, J.L. & SAEMUNDSSON, K. 1975. Relatively old basalts from structurally high areas in central Iceland. *Earth Planet Sci. Lett.*, **28** 83-97.

BAMLETT, M. & POTTER, J.F., 1988. Icelandic Geology; an explanatory excursion guide based on a 1986 field meeting. *Proc. Geol. Ass.*, **99**, 221-48.

BARDARSON, G. 1925. A stratigraphical survey of the Pliocene deposits at Tjörnes in northern Iceland. *Kong, Danske Videske, Selskab, Skr. Medd. Biol.*, 4 (5), 118pp.

BARTH, T.F.W., 1950. *Volcanic Geology, Hot Springs and Geysers of Iceland.* Carnegie Institution, Washington D.C. Publ. 587.

BERGH, S.G. & SIGVALDASON, G.E. 1991. Pleistocene mass flow deposits of basaltic hyaloclastite on a shallow submarine shelf, south Iceland. *Bull Vulcanol.*, **53**, 597-611.

BJORNSSON, A., JOHNSEN, G., SIGURDSSON, S, THORBERGSSON, G. & TRYGGVASON, E. 1979. Rifting of the Plate Boundary in North Iceland 1975-1978. *J. Geophys. Res.*, **84** (B6), 3029-38.

BLUCK, B.J., 1974. Structure and directional properties of some valley sandur deposits in Southern Iceland. *Sedimentol.*, **21**, 533-54.

CAS, R.A.F. & WRIGHT, J.V. 1987. *Volcanic Successions, ancient and modern.* London, Unwin Hyman, p.224 et seq.

COLLINSON, J.D. & THOMPSON, D.B., 1981. *Sedimentary Structures,* London, Unwin Hyman.

COX, K.G., BELL, J.D. & PANKHURST, R.J. 1980. *The Interpretation of Igneous Rocks.* Chapman & Hall.

DECKER, R.W., EINARSSON Th. & PLUMB, R. 1975. Rifting in Iceland: measuring horizontal movements. *Greinar V. Visindalfélag Islendinga,* 63-73.

DEGRAFF, J.M. & AYDIN, A. 1987. Surface morphology of columnar joints and its significance to mechanics and direction of joint growth. *Geol. Soc. Am. Bull.*, **99**, 605-17.

EINARSSON, Th., 1963. Some new observations of the Breidavik deposits in Tjornes. *Jökull,* **13**, 1-9.

Iceland

EINARSSON, Th., HOPKINS, D.M. & DOELL, R.R. 1967. The Stratigraphy of Tjörnes, Northern Iceland and the History of the Bering Land Bridge. In: *The Bering Land Bridge* (Hopkins, D.M., ed.). California: Stanford Univ. Press. 312-25.

EINARSSON, Th., 1974. The Heimaey eruption. Reykjavik, Heimskringla.

FRANCIS, P. 1976. *Volcanoes.* London, Penguin Books.

GERKE, K. 1974. Crustal movements in Myvatn- and in the Thingvallavatn- area, both horizontal and vertical. In: *Geodynamics of I Iceland and the North Atlantic area.* Kristjansson, L. (ed.) Dordrecht. D. Reidel.

GRONVOLD, K., LARSEN, G., EINARSSON, Th., THORARINSSON, S. & SAEMUNDSSON, K. 1983. The Hekla Eruption, 1980-81. *Bull. Volcanol.*, **16**, 349-63.

HOLMES, A. 1965. *Principles of Physical Geology.* London, Thomas Nelson & Sons. Ltd. Fig. 194, p.266.

HONNOREZ, J. & KIRST, P. 1976. Submarine Basaltic Volcanism: Morphometric Parameters for Discriminating Hyaloclastites from Hyalotuffs. *Bull Volcanol*, **39**, 441-465.

JAKOBSSON, S.P. 1976 *The age of the Grimsnes lavas, SW-Iceland.* Reykjavik, Museum of Natural History, Misc. Papers 69.

JONES, J.G. 1969 (for 1968) Intraglacial volcanoes of the Laugarvatn region, south-west Iceland I.*Q.J. Geol. Soc. Lond.*, **124**, 197-221.

JONES, J.G. 1970 Intraglacial volcanoes of the Laugarvatn region, south-west Iceland II. *J. Geol.*, **78**, 127-40.

JONSSON, J. 1982. Notes on the Katla volcanoglacial debris flows. *Jökull*, **32**, 61-8.

KJARTANSSON, G. 1955. Studies of glacial striae in Iceland. *Natturufraedingurinn*, **25**, 154-71.

KJARTANSSON, G. 1967. The Steinsholthlaup, Central South Iceland, on January 15th, 1967. *Jökull*, **17**, 1249-62.

LONG, P.E. & WOOD, B.J. 1986. Structures, textures and cooling histories of Columbia River basalt flows. *Geol. Soc. Am. Bull.*, **97**, 1144-55.

MACDONALD, G.A. 1 1972. *Volcanoes.* New Jersey, Prentic Hall.

Michael Bamlett and John F. Potter

MIYASHIRO, A. 1978. The nature of alkalic rock series. *Contrib. Mineral Petrol.*, **66**, 91-104.

NORTON, P.E.P. 1977. Neogene mollusca of the Tjörnes sequence, Iceland: paleoecology, zonation, correlation. *Malacologica*, **16**, 211-13.

RAPP, A. & ANNERSTEN, L. 1969. Permafrost and tundra polygons in Northern Sweden. In: *The Periglacial Environment* (Pewe, T.L., ed.) Montreal, McGill-Queens Univ. Press

RYAN, M.P. & SAMMIS, C.G., 1978. Cyclic fracture mechanisms in cooling basalt. *Geol. Soc. Am. Bull.*, **89**, 1295-1308.

SAEMUNDSSON, K. 1970. Intraglacial lava flows in the lowlands of southern Iceland and the Problem of Two-Tiered Columnar Jointing. *Jökull*, **20**, 62-77.

SAEMUNDSSON, K. 1974. Evolution of the Axial Rifting Zone in Northern Iceland and the Tjörnes Fracture Zone. *Geol. Soc. Am. Bull.*, **85**, 495-504.

SAEMUNDSSON, K. 1979. Outline of the geology of Iceland. *Jökull*, **29**, 7-28.

SELF, S., SPARKS, R.S.J., BOOTH, B. & WALKER, G.P.L. 1974. The 1973 Heimaey Strombolian Scoria deposit, Iceland. *Geol. Mag.*, **111**, 539-48.

SIGURDSSON, H. 1982. Volcanic pollution and climate: the 1783 Laki eruption, *Eos*, **63**, 601-2.

SIGVALDASON, G.E. & OSKARSSON, N. 1986. Fluorine in basalts from Iceland. *Contrib. Mineral. Petrol.*, **94**, 263-71.

SPARKS, R.S.J., WILSON, L. & SIGURDSSON, H. 1981. The pyroclastic deposits of the 1875 eruption of Askja, Iceland. *Phil. Trans. Royal Soc. London.*, **A299**, 241-73.

THORARINSSON, S. 1957. The Jökulhlaup from the Katla area in 1955 compared with other Jökulhlaups in Iceland. *Jökull*, **7**, 21-25.

THORARINSSON, S. 1964. Additional notes on patterned ground in Iceland with a particular reference to ice-wedge polygons. *Biul. Peryglac.*, **14**, 327-36.

THORARINSSON, S. 1969a. *A Pleistocene ignimbrite in Thórsmörk.* Reykjavik., Mus. Nat. Hist. Misc. Paper 59.

THORARINSSON, S. 1969b. The Lakagigar Eruption on 1783. *Bull. Volcanol.*, **33**, 910-29.

TRYGGVASON, E. 1980. Subsidence events in the Krafla area, North Iceland, 1975-1979. *J. Geophys.*, **47**, 141-53.

THORARINSSON, S. 1969a. *A Pleistocene ignimbrite in Thórsmörk.* Reuykjavic., Mus. Nat. Hist. Misc. Paper 59.

THORARINSSON, S. 1969b. The Lakagigar Eruption on 1783. *Bull. Volcanol.*, **33**, 910-29.

TRYGGVASON, E. 1980. Subsidence events in the Krafla area, North Iceland, 1975-1979. *J. Geophys.*, **47**, 141-53.

WALKER, G.P.L., 1959 (for 1958) Geology of the Reydarfjördur area, eastern Iceland. *Q.J. Geol. Soc. Lond.*, **114**, 367-93.

WALKER, G.P.L., 1960. Zeolite zones and dike distribution in relation to the structure of the basalts in eastern Iceland. *J. Geol.*, **68**, 515-28.

WALKER, G.P.L., 1963. The Breiddalur central volcano, eastern Iceland. *Q.J. Geol. Soc. Lond.*, **119**, 29-63.

WASHBURN, A.L. 1956. Classification of patterned ground and review of suggested origins. *Geol. Soc. Am. Bull.*, **67**, 823-66.

WOOD, C. 1971. The nature and origin of Raufarholschellir. *Trans. Cave Res. Gp. G.B.*, 13, 245-56.

Michael Bamlett and John F. Potter

GLOSSARY

ANKARAMITE. A dark coloured porphyritic basalt with abundant phenocrysts of pyroxene and olivine.

BASAL SURGE DEPOSIT. Material deposited quickly by a horizontal blast from a volcanic explosive eruption.

B.P.   Years before the present day.

BOLE.   See Paleosol.

CALDERA. Subsidence structure, usually formed by the collapse of a volcanic field into the void created by the eruption of large volumes of lava.

CENTRAL VOLCANO. One with a generally circular plan and the main crater in the centre of the circle.

CHALCEDONY. A glassy precipitate of silica, SiO_2.

CIRQUE.   The amphitheatre-shaped feature at the head of some glaciers.

DACITE.   A volcanic rock composed of sodic plagioclase with minor amounts of biotite, hornblende or pyroxene. Equivalent chemically to a granodiorite.

DIAMICTITE. A lithified flow of mud and rock fragments originally set in motion by heavy rain which accompanied a volcanic eruption.

DRUMLIN. An ice-smoothed hillock of morainic material, with the blunt end facing up-stream to the ice movement.

ESKER.   A winding ridge of gravel and sand, originally deposited by a meltwater stream flowing beneath or within a glacier.

FELSITE, FELSITIC. Acid, igneous rock- a general field term for any fine grained igneous rock rich in silica.

FIAMMÉ.   Lens-shaped fragments of lava or pumice in a deposit resulting from a major volcanic explosion which generated a strong horizontal blast (base surge).

GRABEN.   A rift valley, subsided between two normal/tensional faults.

GRANOPHYRE. A porphyritic rock of granitic composition in which phenocrysts, commonly alkali feldspar, are set in a matrix of micrographic (branching) intergrowths of alkali feldspar and quartz.

HYALOCLASTITE. The product of interaction between subaerially-erupted basaltic lava, when the latter flows into the sea or a lake. Also sometimes called palagonite or hydrated basaltic glass.

HYDROTHERMAL. Usually applied to mineral deposits (e.g. zeolites here) resulting from the precipitation of solids from a cooling and ascending plume of naturally (geothermally) heated water through the voids and planar pathways in a rock body.

ICELANDITE. A variety of intermediate volcanic rock akin to andesite, containing phenocrysts of andesine, pyroxene, pigeonite and occasionally olivine in a groundmass of smaller crystals of the same minerals. It differs from normal andesite in having less aluminium and more iron.

IGNIMBRITE. An indurated (usually) tuff, comprising crystal and rock fragments often welded together by a matrix of glass shards. Usually acid to intermediate in its chemistry.

ISOSTATIC. Movement of a crustal block in relation to its underlying section of the earth. Best perceived as the vertical variation of such a block in terms of it 'floating' on a fluid medium, although this is not in fact the case. Iceland was depressed by the weight of its former total ice cover and has risen since most of this has melted.

KETTLE HOLE. Small depression in a morainic deposit formed by blocks of ice being left behind when the overall ice cover melted. These blocks eventually melted, leaving their 'nests' behind them in the moraine.

LACCOLITH. An igneous intrusion which resembles a buried shield volcano- a modified form of sill.

LIGNITE. Compressed and poorly lithified vegetation. A poor coal.

MORAINE, MORAINIC DEPOSIT. Boulders, gravel, sand and clay which were once incorporated in a glacier or ice sheet and were deposited on the land surface when the ice melted, often as low hills or ridges. (See esker, drumlin).

OUTWASH PLAIN. Flat land downstream from a terminal moraine. Often sandy and dissected by streams.

PALEOSOL (or Bole). Ancient, buried soils, developed on the surface of lava flows and often found buried beneath subsequent flows.

PHENOCRYSTS. Large crystals of a particular mineral in a matrix of smaller crystals or glass, forming a PORPHYRY.

PLINIAN. A type of volcanic eruption characterised by enormous volumes of fragmentary rock ejected in an explosive event resulting from a gas eruption. Most of this material settles as volcanic ash on the surrounding area.

PLUMOSE. Having the shape of a plume of feathers, narrow at the base and becoming wider towards the top.

PORPHYRY. See Phenocrysts. A rock with a porphyritic texture.

RAISED BEACH. An area of land which was once sub-tidal or intertidal and is now unaffected by the tidal activity. Often has a former sea cliff on its landward side. May result from isostatic elevation.

RECESSION GORGE. Waterfalls retreat upstream by eroding the lip of the fall. In doing so they leave a gorge downstream from the existing fall. This is the recession gorge.

RHYOLITE. Highly siliceous volcanic rock often containing phenocrysts of quartz and alkali feldspar in a microcrystalline or glassy matrix. Chemistry same as granite.

ROCHES MOUTONÉES. Ice-smoothed and scratched outcrops of rock, now revealed from beneath the ice after it melted. The blunt end faces downstream in relation to the former ice stream.

SAG STRUCTURES. Impact marks made by rocks falling into soft sediments.

SCORIA. Cindery lava deposits, resulting from gas-rich explosive eruptions. Looks rather like slag from a blast furnace.

SHIELD VOLCANO. A central volcano characterised by a gently-sloping cone caused by the eruption of non-explosive, rapidly-moving, basaltic lavas.

SPINDLE BOMBS. Forcefully expelled blocks of rotating plastic lava with a spindle shape.

STROMBOLIAN. A type of volcanic eruption characterised by large amounts of gas and scoria, which usually settles around the crater or falls back into it. Little in the way of lava flows are generated.

SURTSEYAN. A violent eruption due to reaction between magma and large volumes of water. Fragmented products contain a high proportion of very small particles.

TEPHRA. Fragmental material of all sizes emitted from volcanoes by explosive eruptions. Includes blocks, 'bombs', cinders and ash.

THOLEIITE. A hypersthene-bearing basalt which may contain olivine.

TILL, TILLITE. A widespread, often rather featureless type of morainic material, dominated by clay and sand, with boulders. Tillite is a lithified till.

TUFF. A pyroclastic rock in which the average pyroclast size is between 2mm and 1/16mm. Ash tuff means the same as tuff. Modern usage sometimes uses this term to include lithified deposits.

VESICULAR. A texture produced in igneous rocks by ovoid and irregular gas cavities.

Michael Bamlett and John F. Potter

APPENDIX

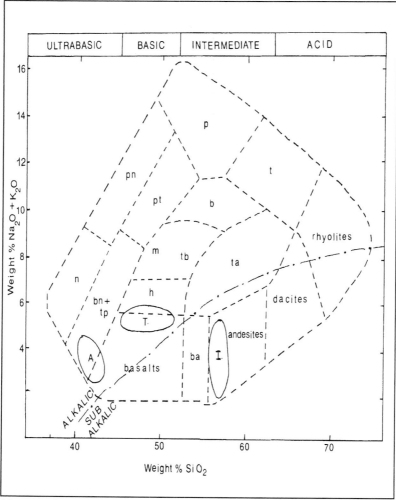

Names and approximate compositions of non-potassic lavas after Cox et al, 1979, with the addition of 3, non-standard Icelandic types. A = Ankaramite; T = Tholeiitic basalt; ba = basaltic andesite; I = Icelandite. Names written out in full are also found in Iceland. Others are rare or absent. Alkalic/sub-alkalic dividing line is from Miyas hiro (1978).